Bastiens' Invitation to Music

For:
Ages 4-7

Time:
A Lifetime of Enjoyment

Hosts:
Jane Smisor Bastien
Lisa Bastien
Lori Bastien

kjos
Neil A. Kjos Music Company, Publisher

BOOK B

THEORY & EAR TRAINING PARTY

CONTENTS

ISBN 0-8497-9554-0

REVIEWING WHITE KEYS

Write the letter names of the shaded keys on each house.

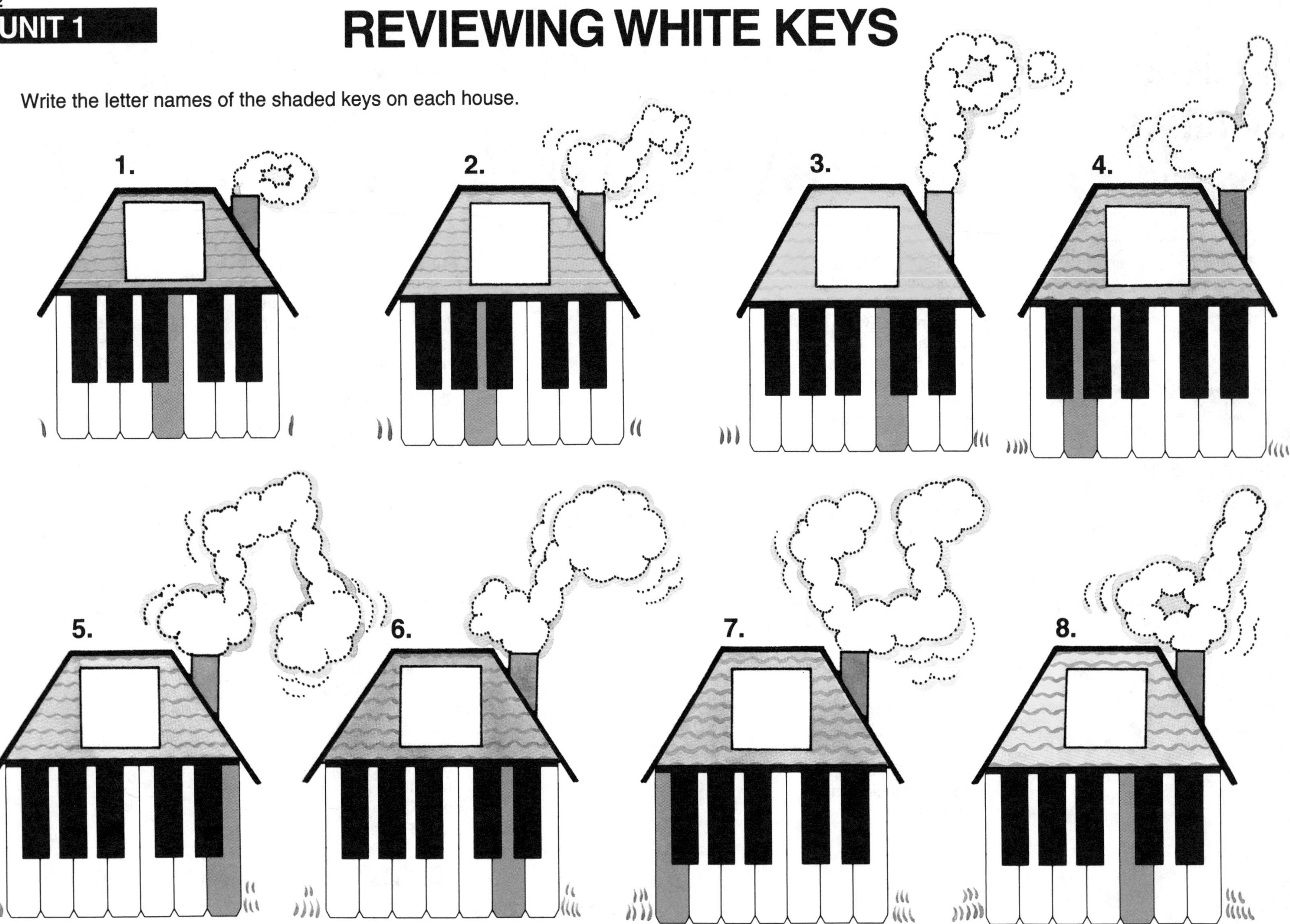

ALPHABET FILL-INS

Think of the music alphabet going **up** on the keyboard and fill in the missing letters.

RECOGNIZING TWO C POSITIONS

Circle:

- C 5-finger positions red
- Middle C positions blue

CHIMES

1.

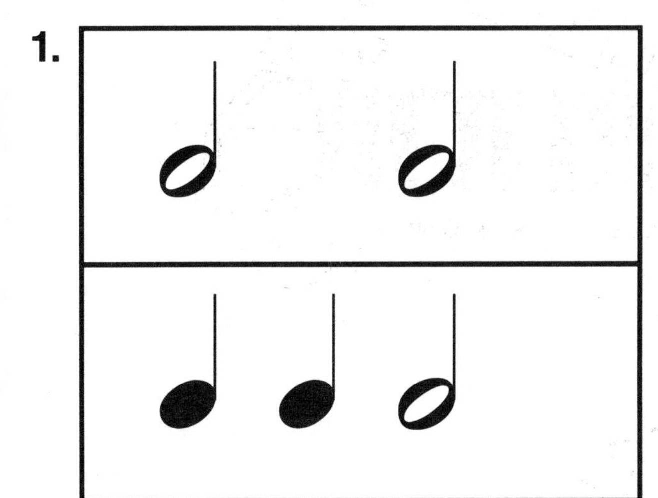

2.

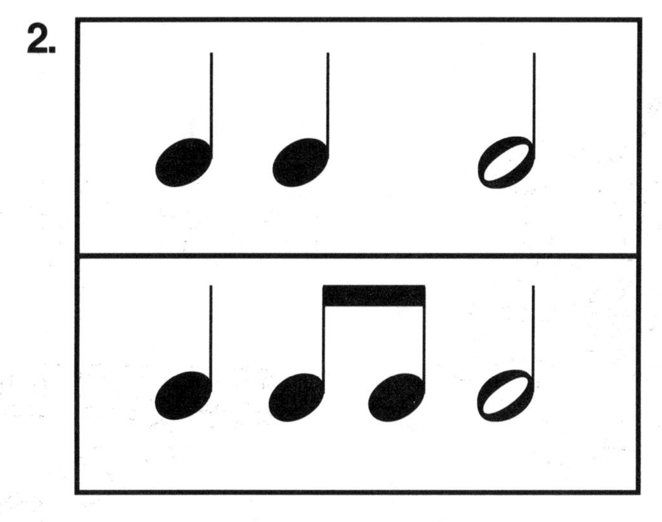

3.

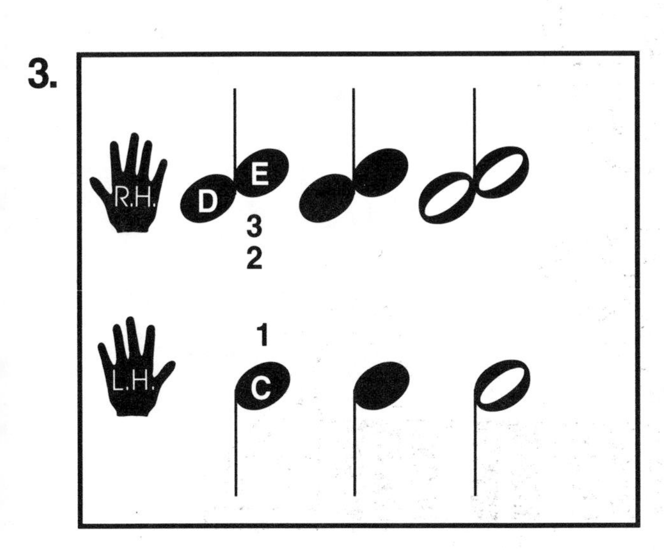

4.

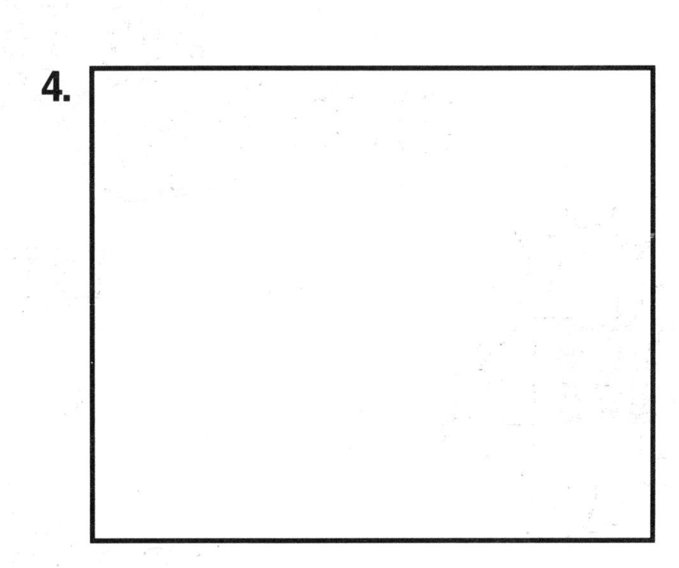

UNIT 1

Teacher's Notes page 46

EAR TRAINING

TEDDY BEAR'S RAINY DAY

Color:
- E's orange
- G's green
- C's blue
- D's red
- F's purple

1.

2.

3.

4.

THE WOODPECKER'S SONG

UNIT 1
Teacher's Notes page 46
EAR TRAINING

UNIT 2

WRITING TWO C POSITIONS

1. Write the letter names of the Middle C position for each hand.

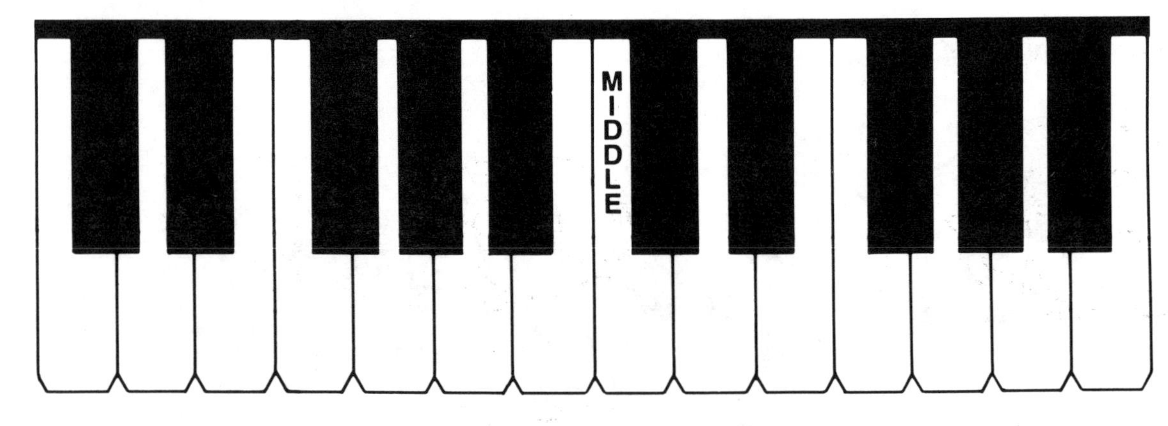

2. Write the letter names of the C 5-finger position for each hand.

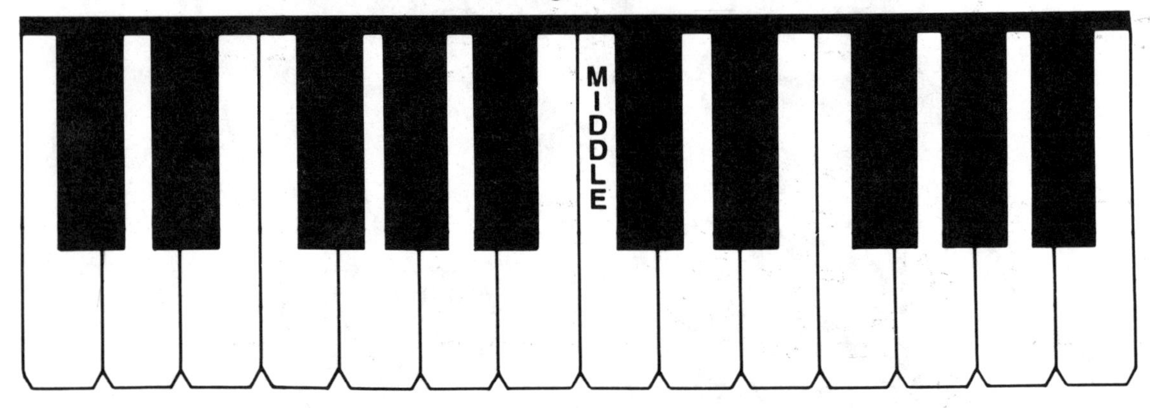

3. On both keyboards, color:

- E's brown
- B's yellow
- G's green
- D's red
- C's purple
- F's blue
- A's orange

ALPHABET FILL-INS

Think of the music alphabet going **down** on the keyboard and fill in the missing letters.

UNIT 2
Teacher's Notes page 47
EAR TRAINING

MATCHING C POSITIONS

1.

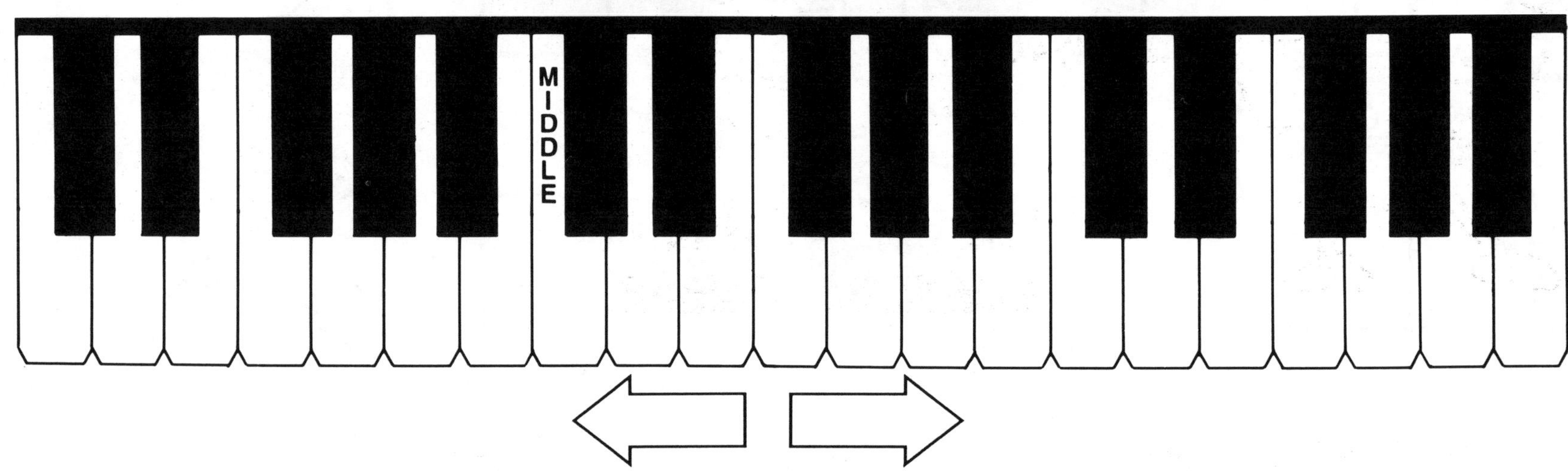

2.

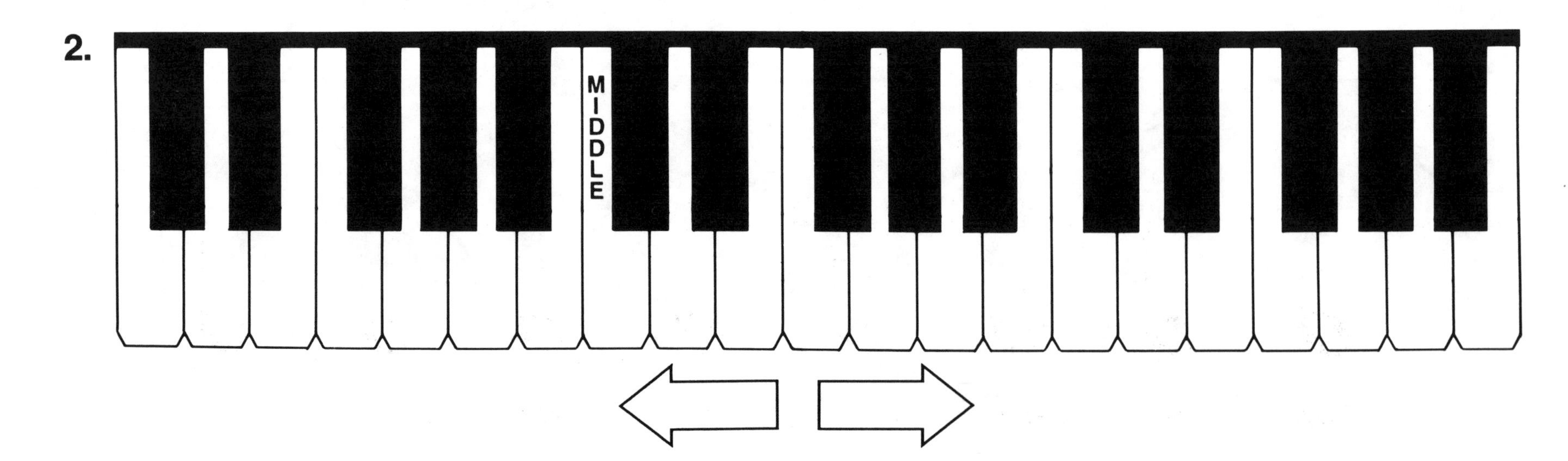

TAP AND CLAP FILL-INS

RECOGNIZING STEPS AND SKIPS

1.

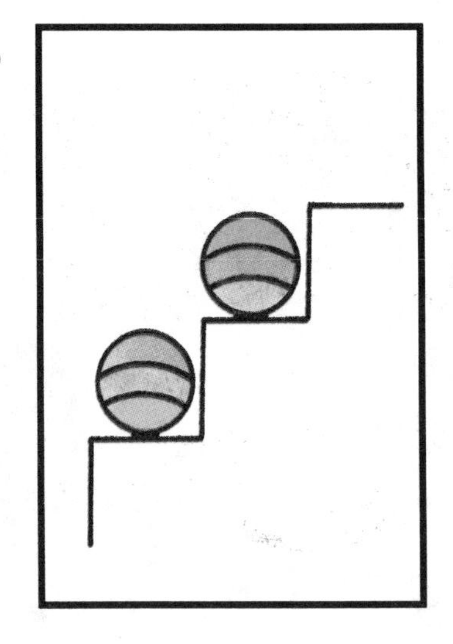

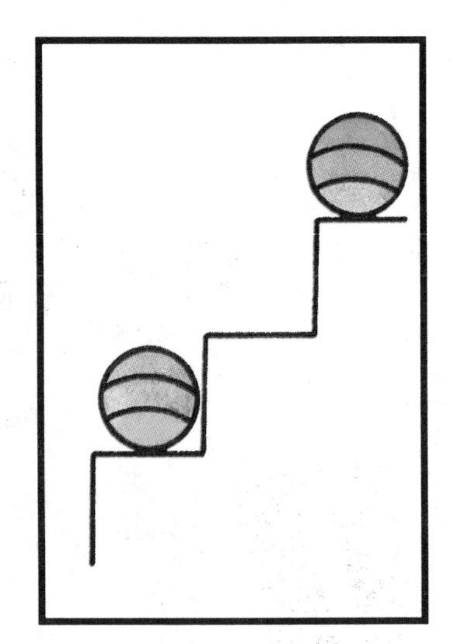

2.

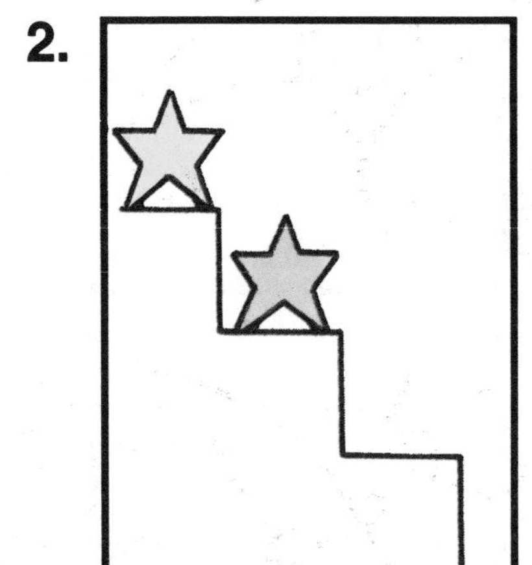

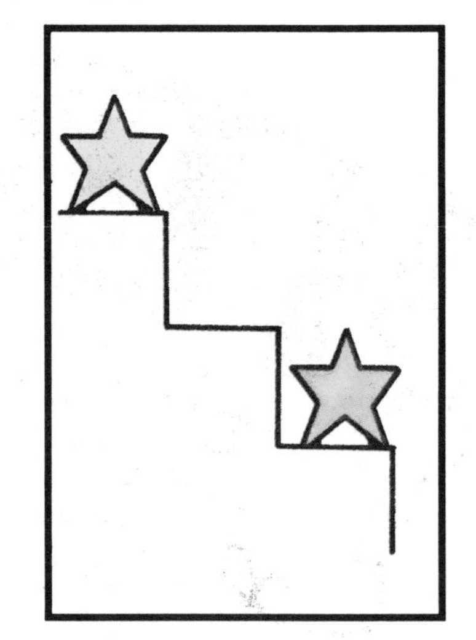

3.

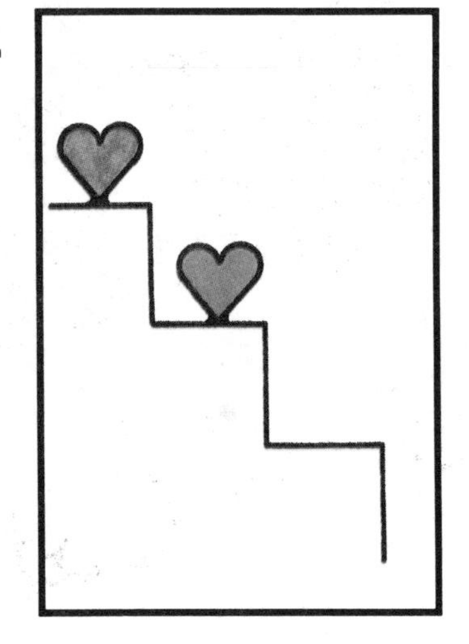

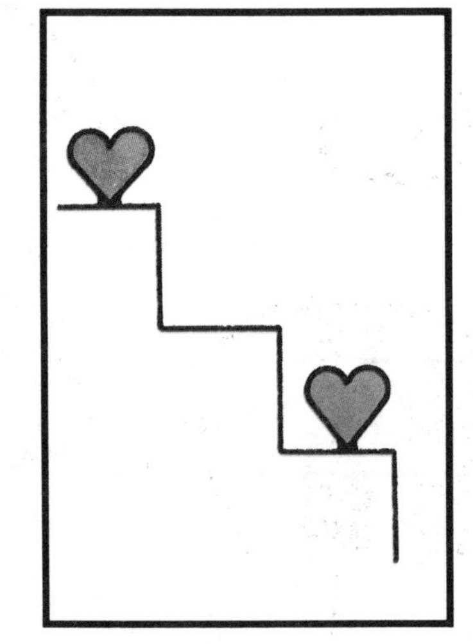

4.

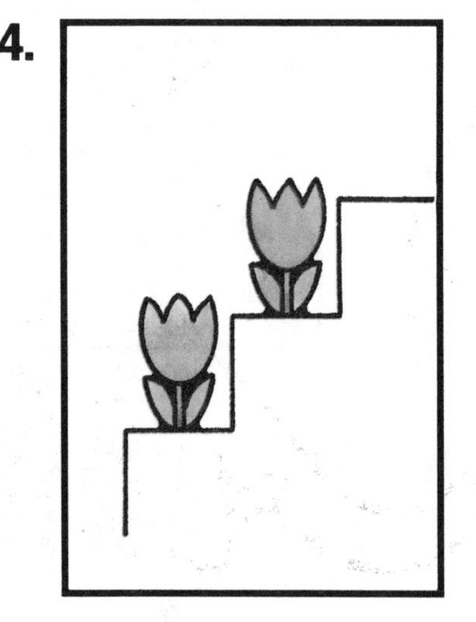

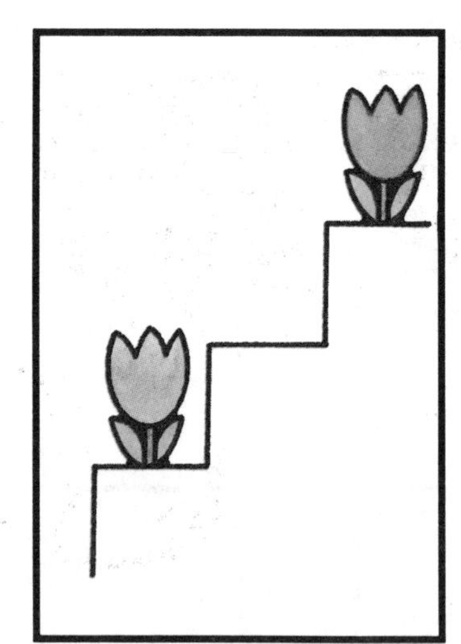

WRITING STEPS AND SKIPS

Write letter names on the keyboards to form steps and skips as indicated.

MUSIC ALPHABET UP AND DOWN

Write the music alphabet going **up** the keyboard beginning with the given letters.

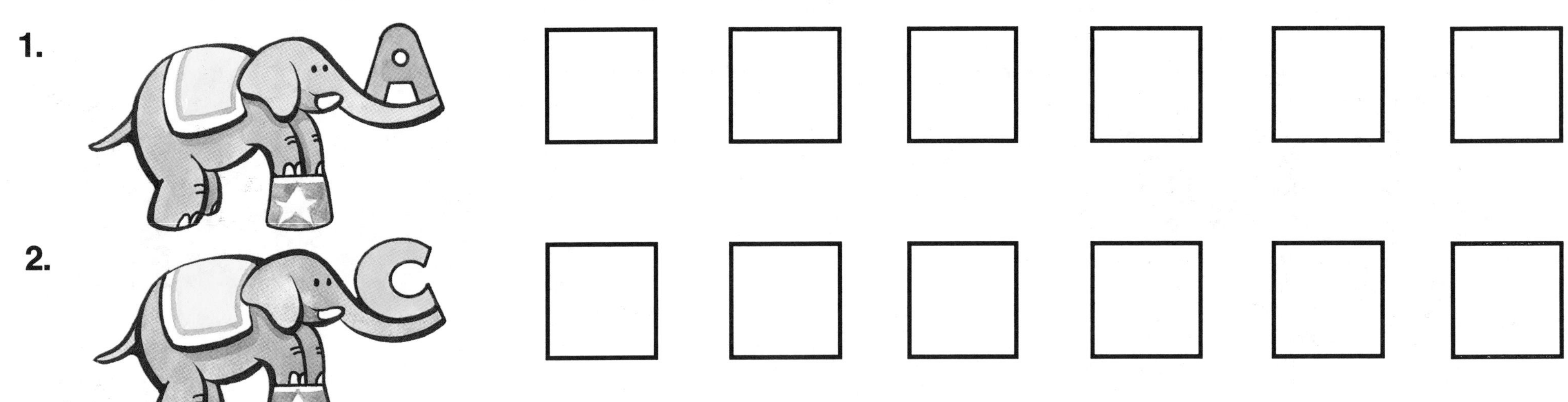

Write the music alphabet going **down** the keyboard beginning with the given letters.

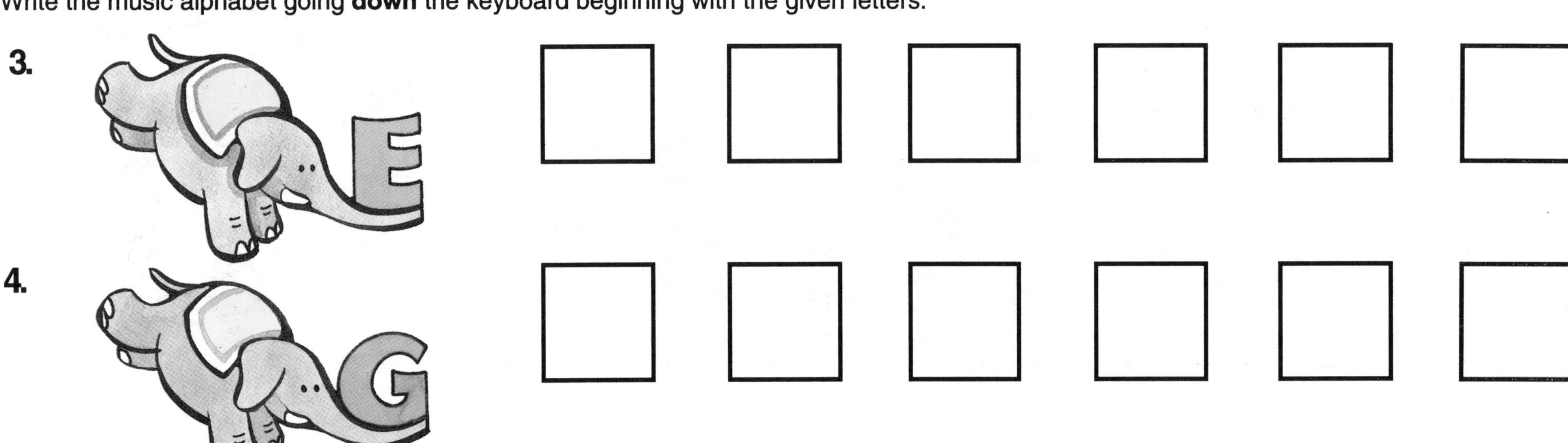

WRITING AND HEARING C CHORDS

A I chord has two skips.

MELODIC HOWLS

THE BLUEBIRD'S SONG

1.

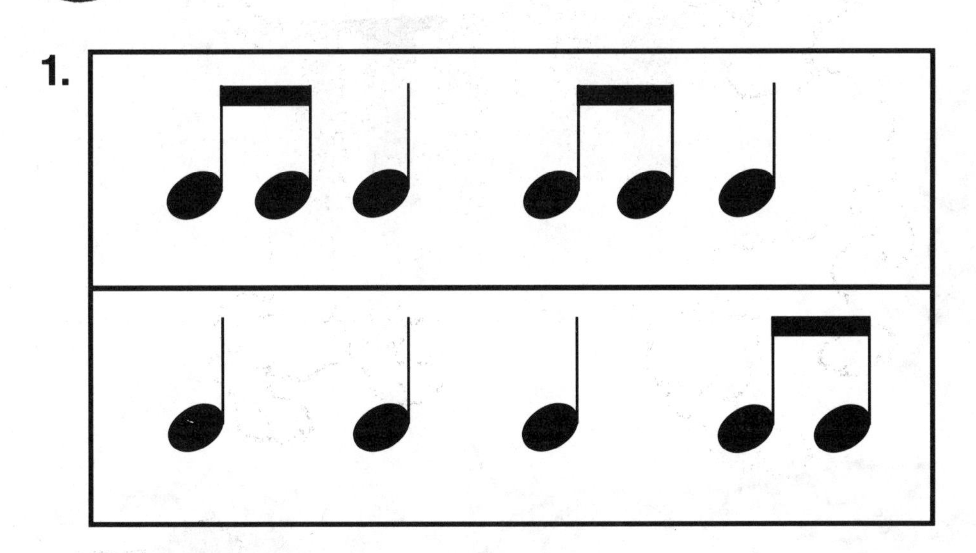

2.

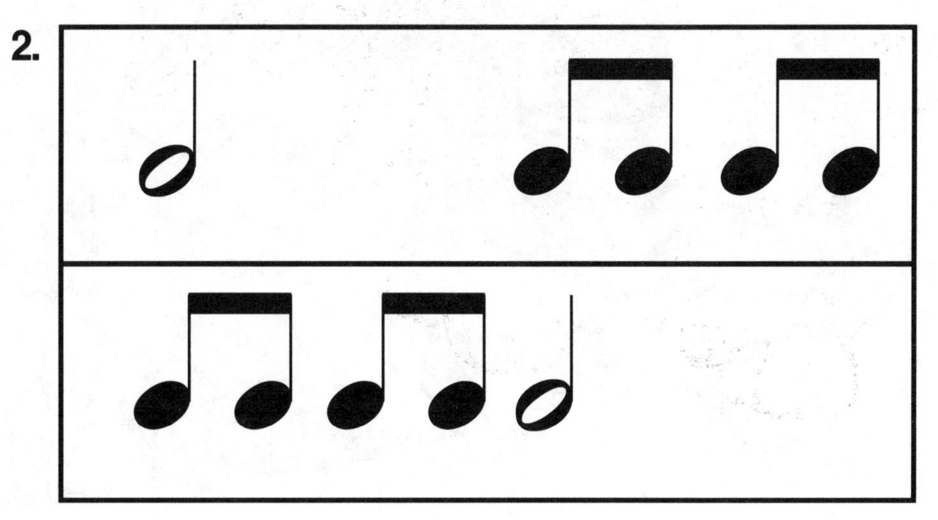

3.

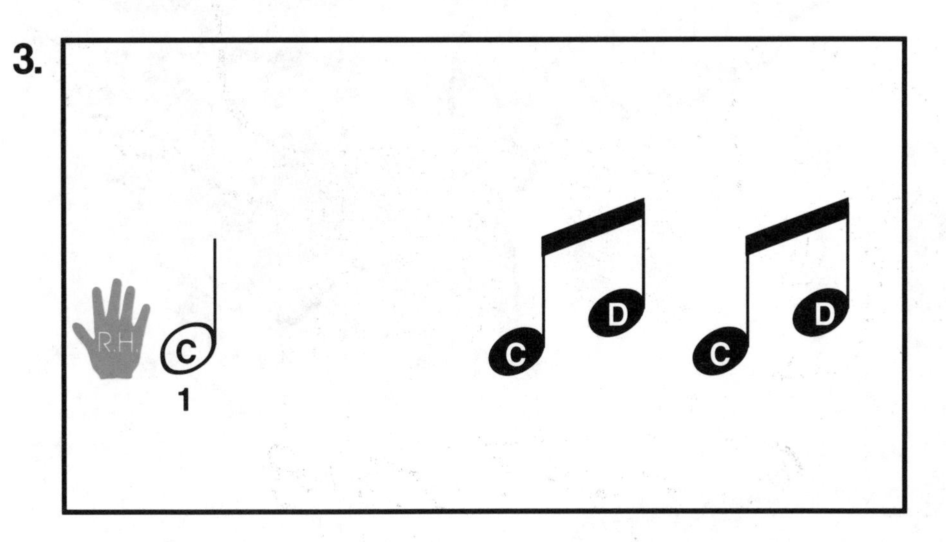

4.

WRITING THE G POSITION

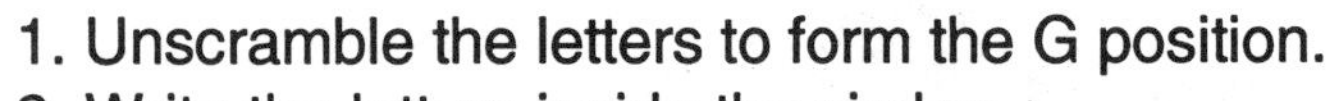

1. Unscramble the letters to form the G position.
2. Write the letters inside the circles.

Write the letter names of the G 5-finger position for each hand on this keyboard.
Color the keys ■ red to form I chords for each hand.

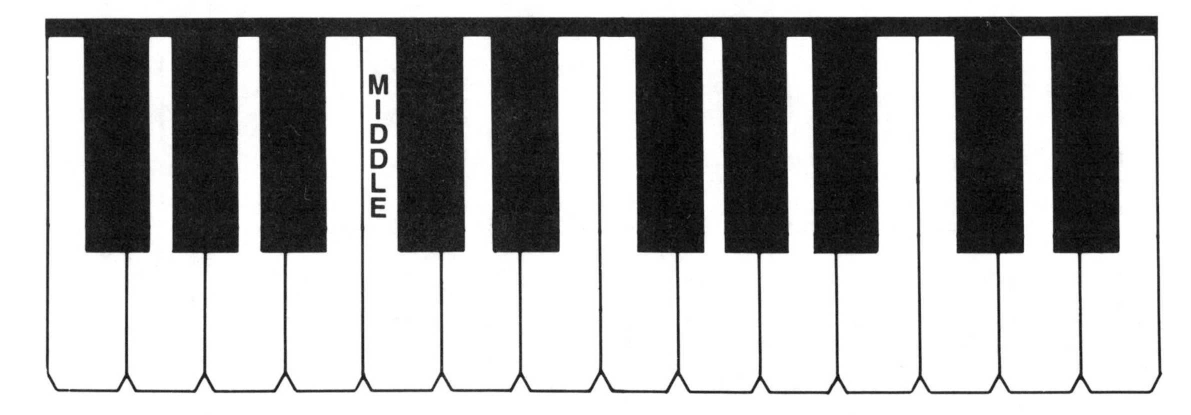

RECOGNIZING AND DRAWING NOTES

Color the dinosaurs with:
- dotted quarter notes red
- three eighth notes blue
- single eighth notes green

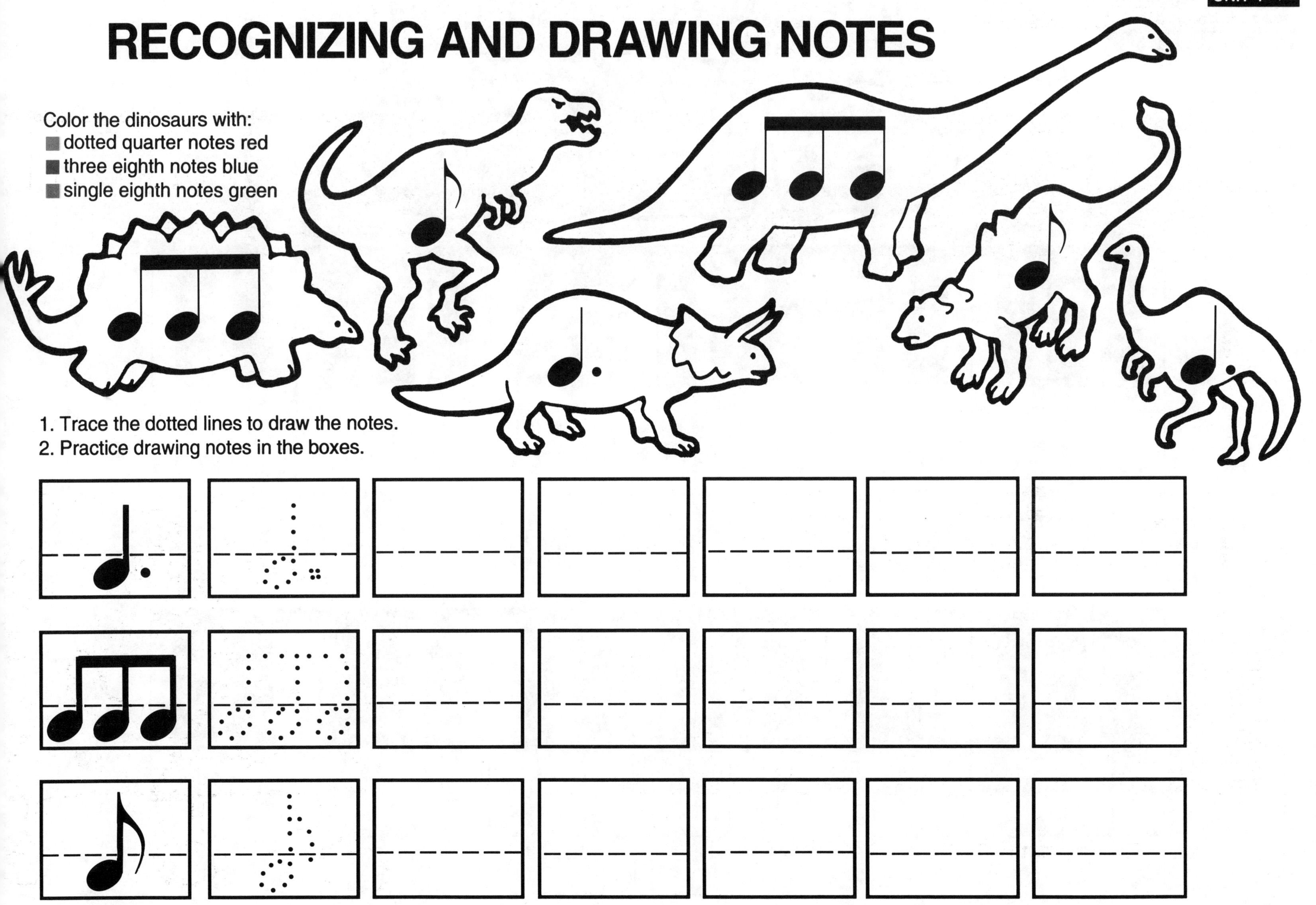

1. Trace the dotted lines to draw the notes.
2. Practice drawing notes in the boxes.

Teacher's Notes page 48

MATCHING G POSITIONS

1.

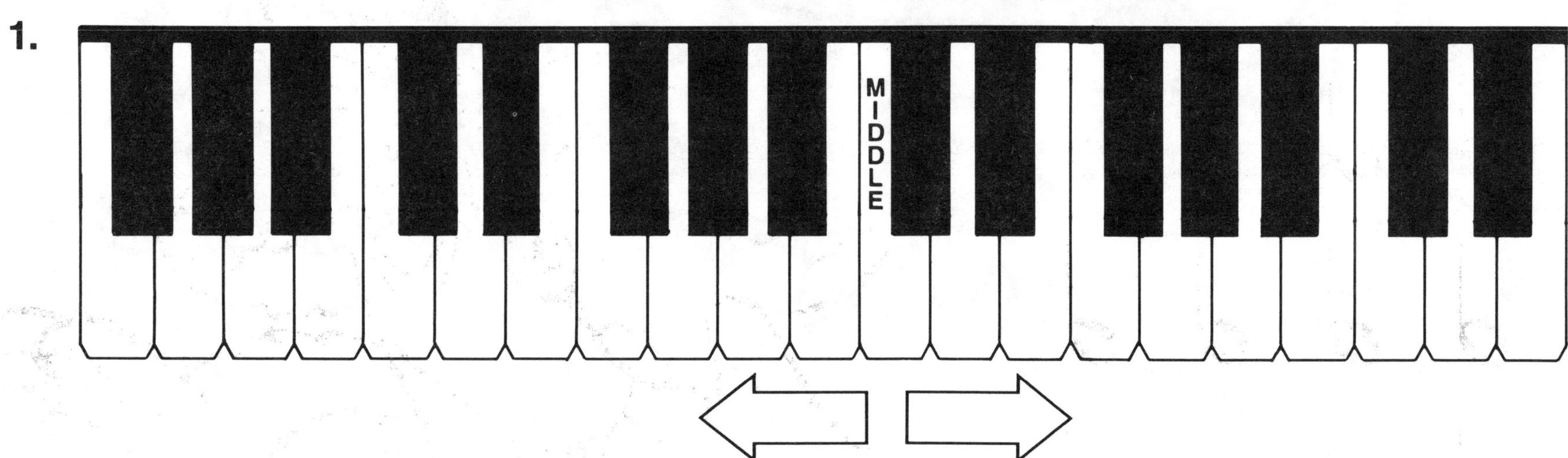

2.

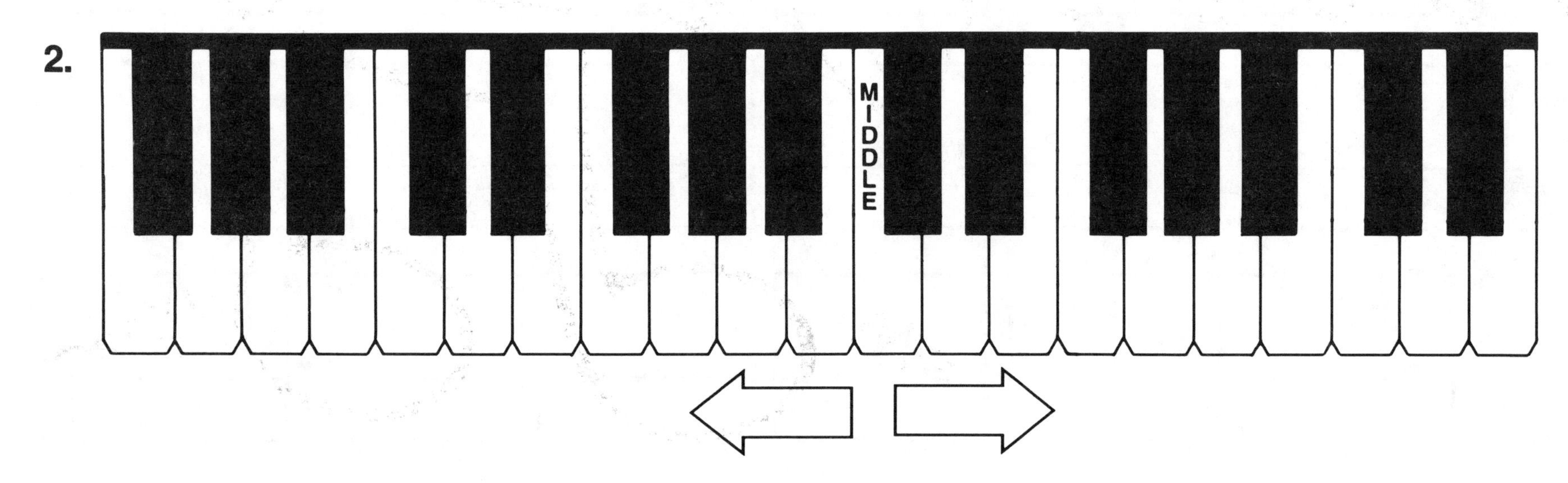

BOOGIE WOOGIE BUNNY

HANDY ANDY

1.

2.

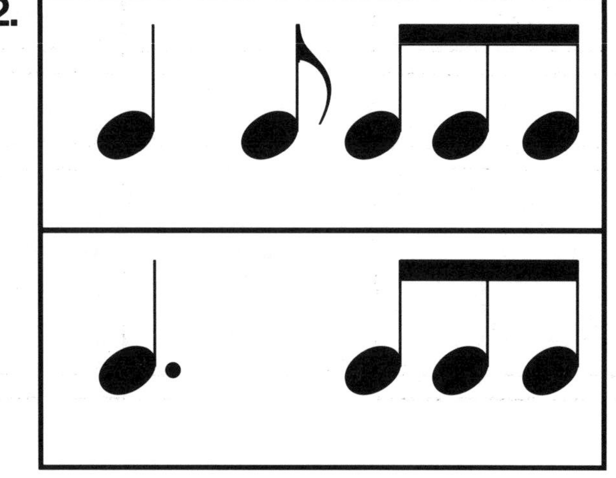

3.

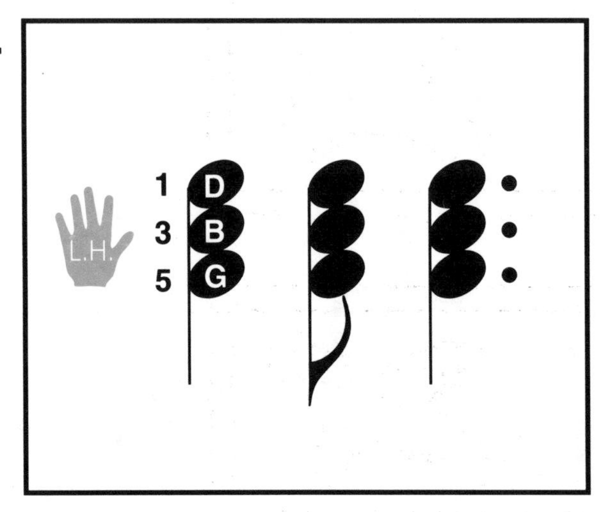

4.

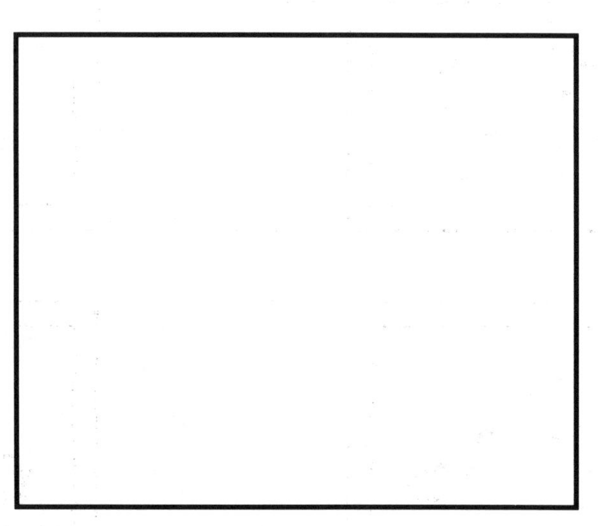

ALPHABET SKIPS

Write letters to form alphabet skips **up** from the given letter.
Whisper the letters you skip when you see the arrows.

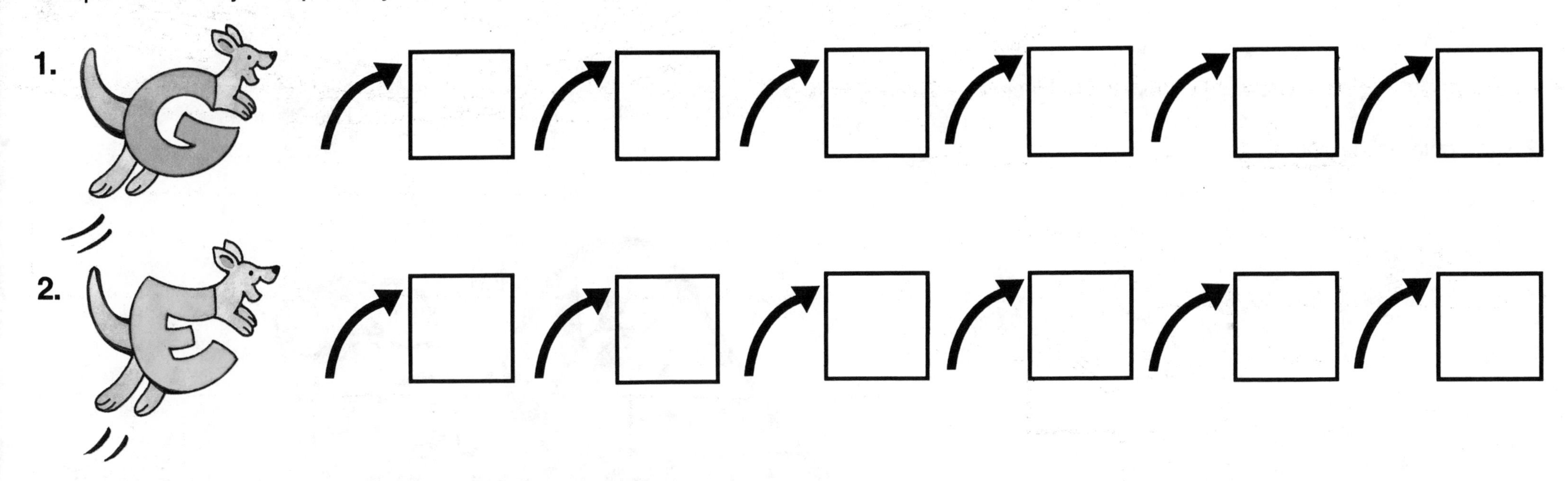

Write letters to form alphabet skips **down** from the given letter.
Whisper the letters you skip when you see the arrows.

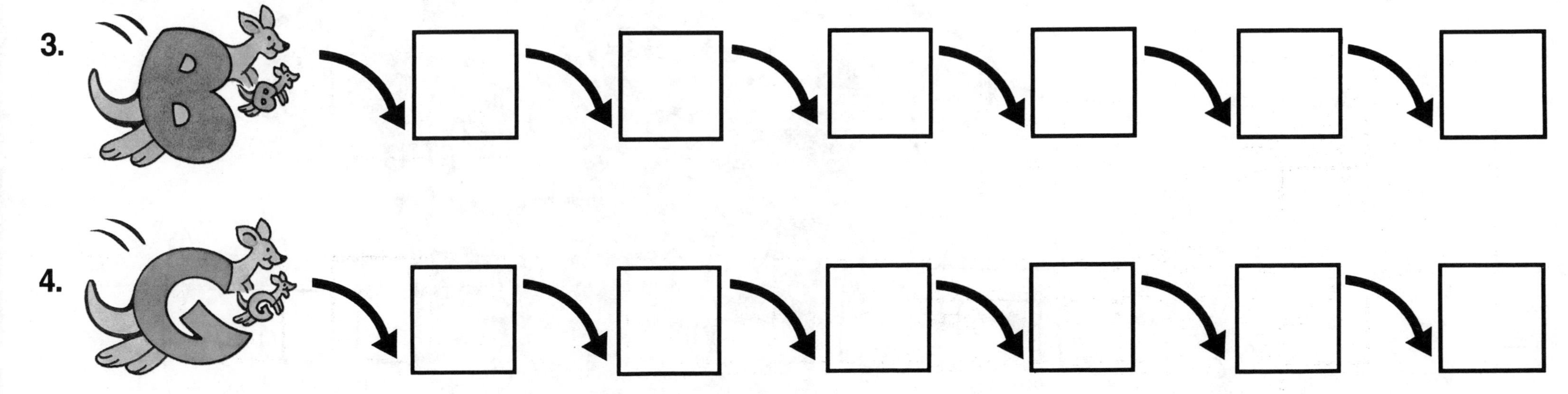

THE GINGERBREAD NOTE HOUSE

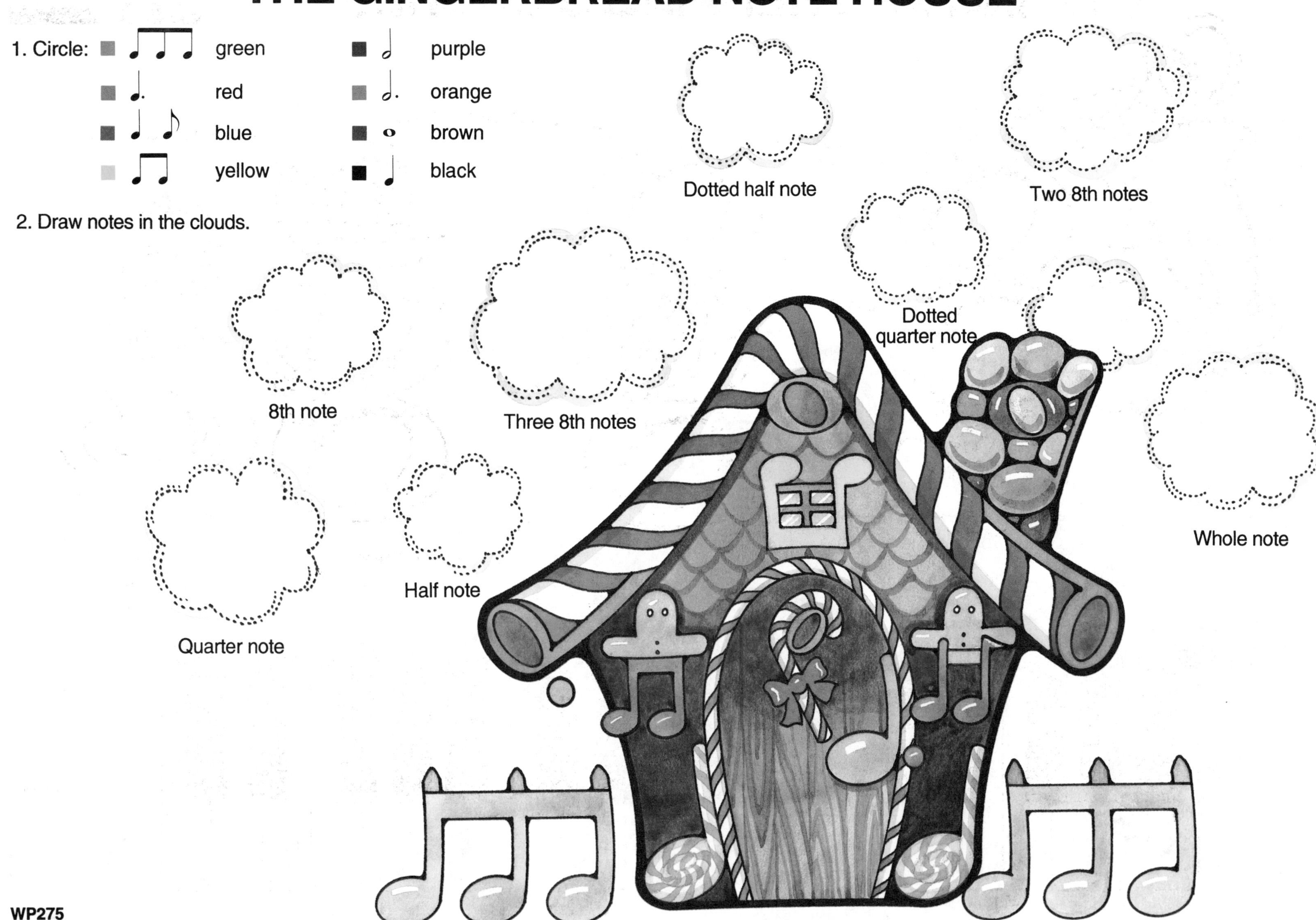

UNIT 5
Teacher's Notes page 49
EAR TRAINING

WRITING AND HEARING G CHORDS

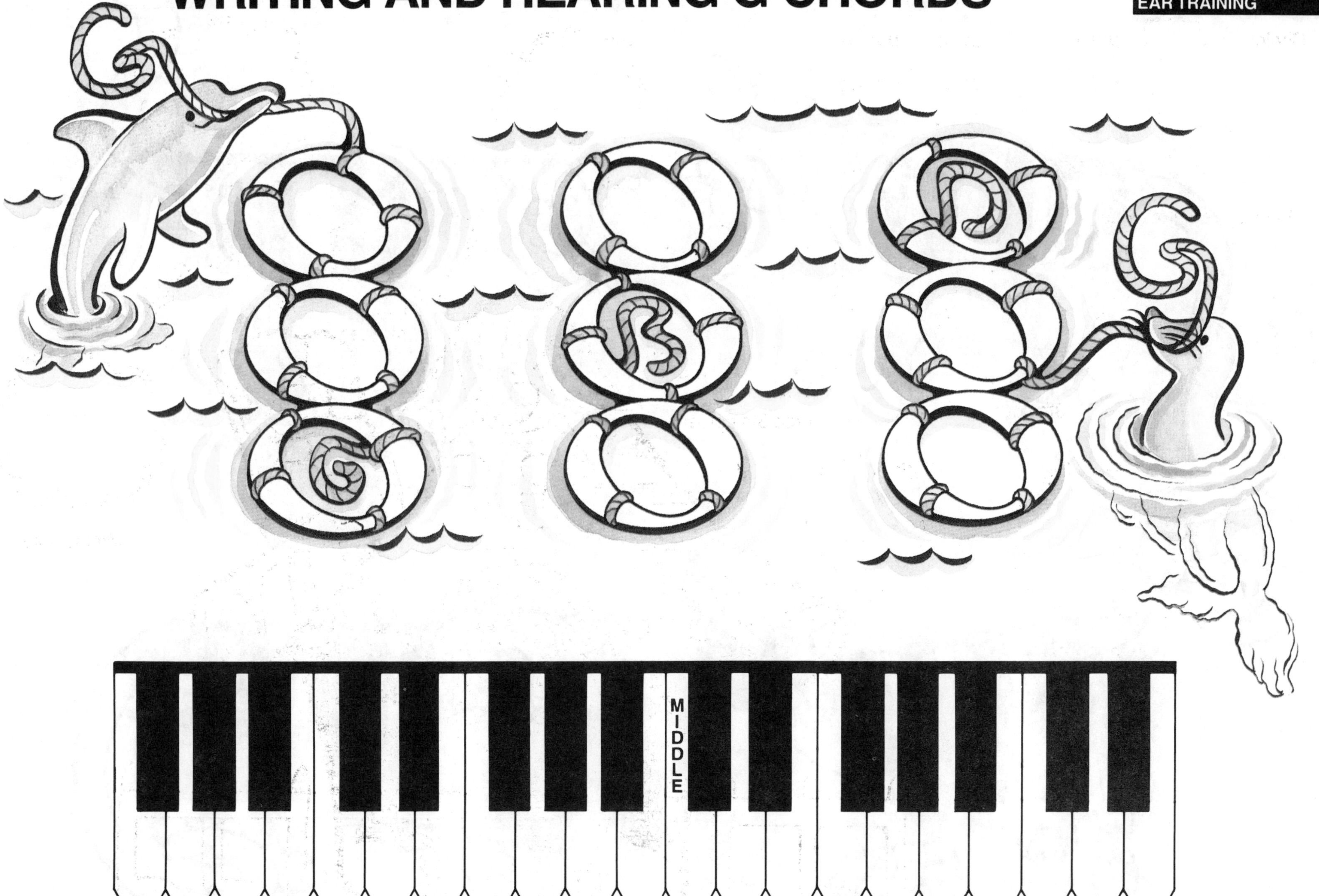

MELODIC MEOWS

1.

G

2.

D

3.

B

4.

A

THE GIFTS OF MUSIC

COLORING AND NAMING FLATS

Color the correct keys black.

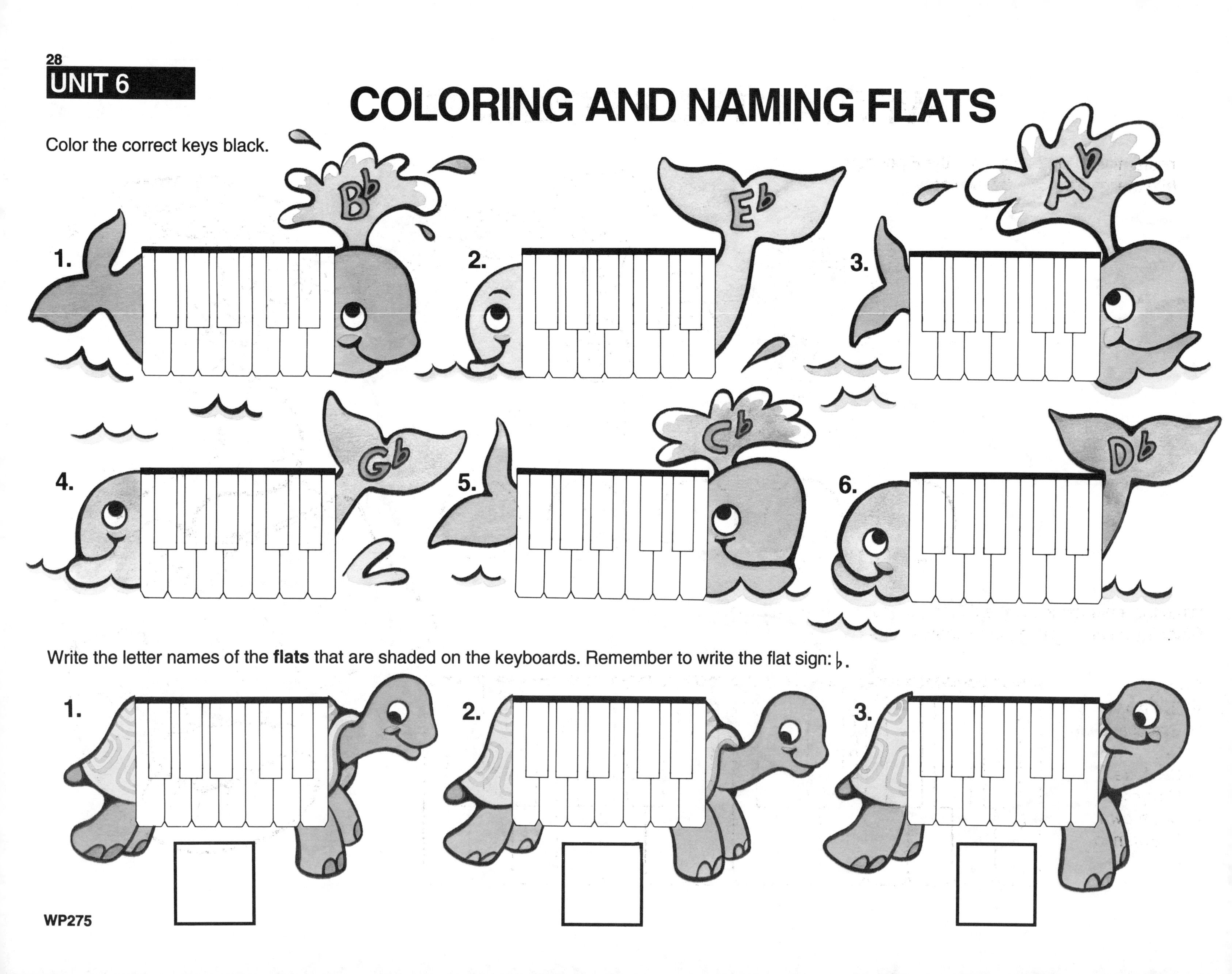

Write the letter names of the **flats** that are shaded on the keyboards. Remember to write the flat sign: ♭.

WRITING THE F POSITION

1. Unscramble the letters to form the F position
2. Write the letters inside the circles.

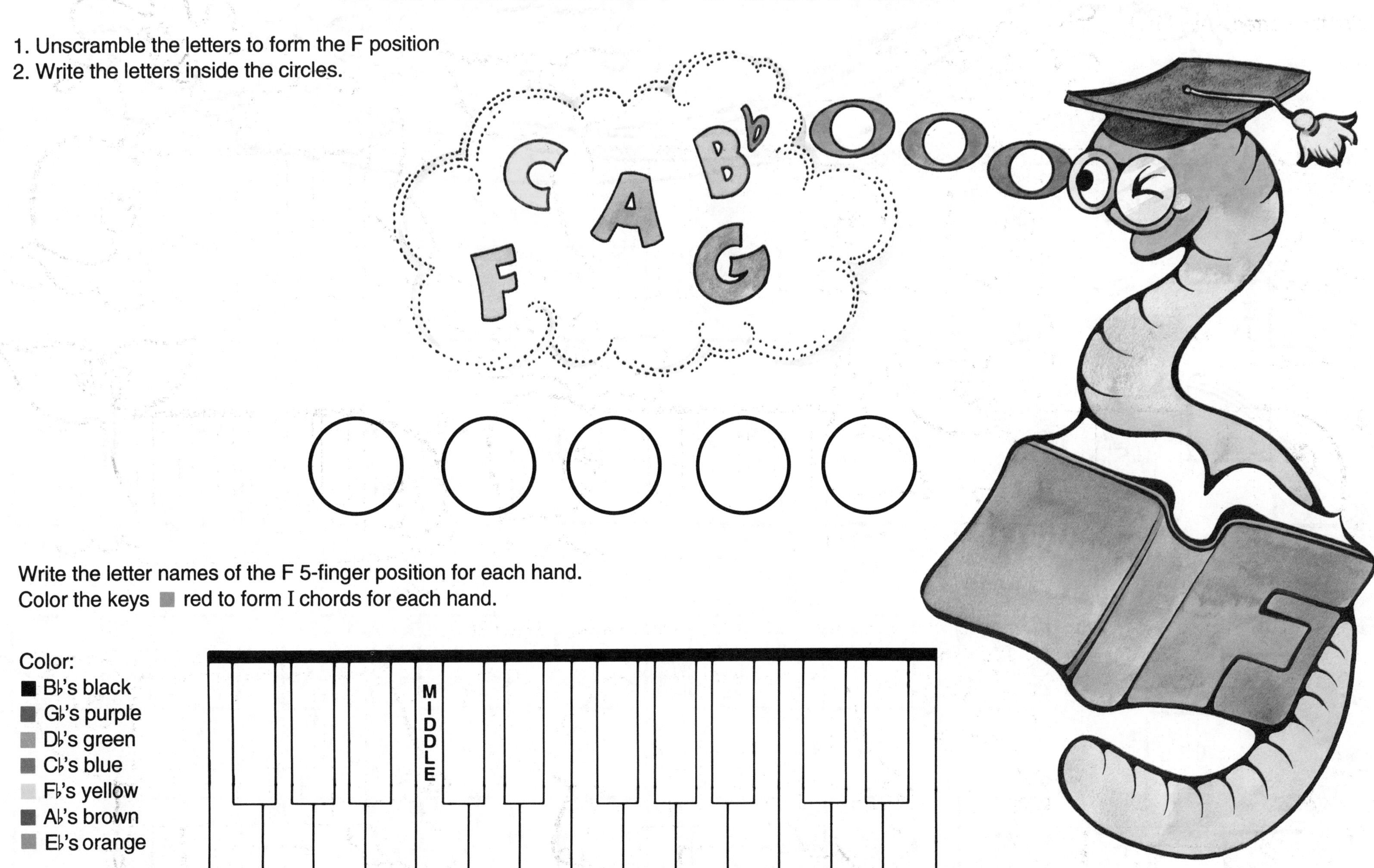

Write the letter names of the F 5-finger position for each hand.
Color the keys ■ red to form I chords for each hand.

Color:
- ■ B♭'s black
- ■ G♭'s purple
- ■ D♭'s green
- ■ C♭'s blue
- ■ F♭'s yellow
- ■ A♭'s brown
- ■ E♭'s orange

WATER SLIDE

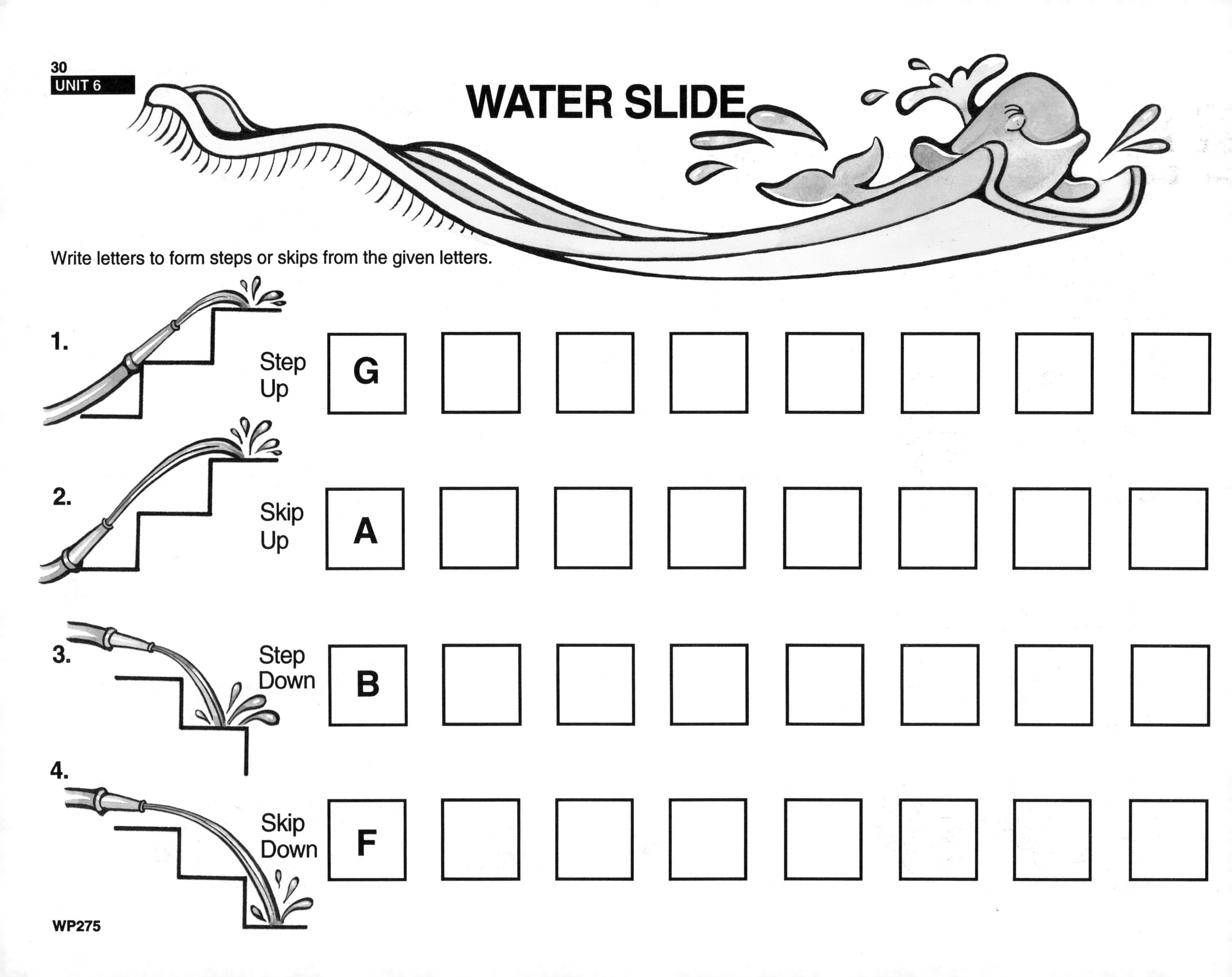

Write letters to form steps or skips from the given letters.

1. Step Up

G							

2. Skip Up

A							

3. Step Down

B							

4. Skip Down

F							

UNIT 6
Teacher's Notes page 50
EAR TRAINING

SAME AND DIFFERENT

1.

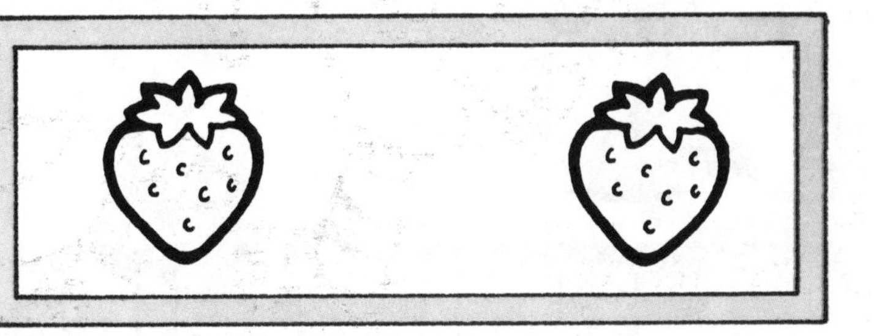

2.

3.

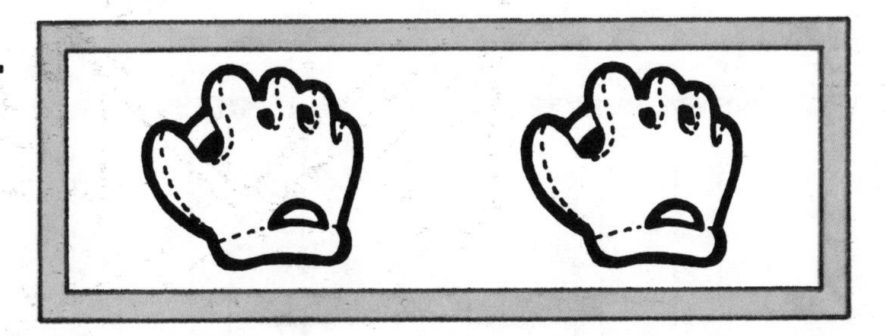

4.

MATCHING F POSITIONS

1.

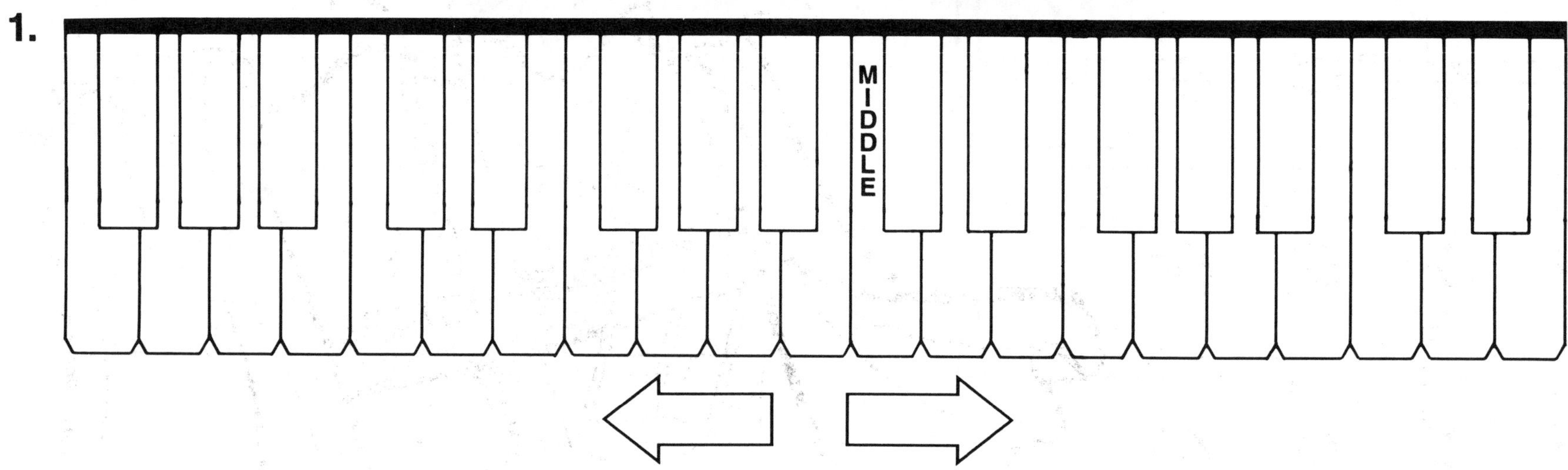

2.

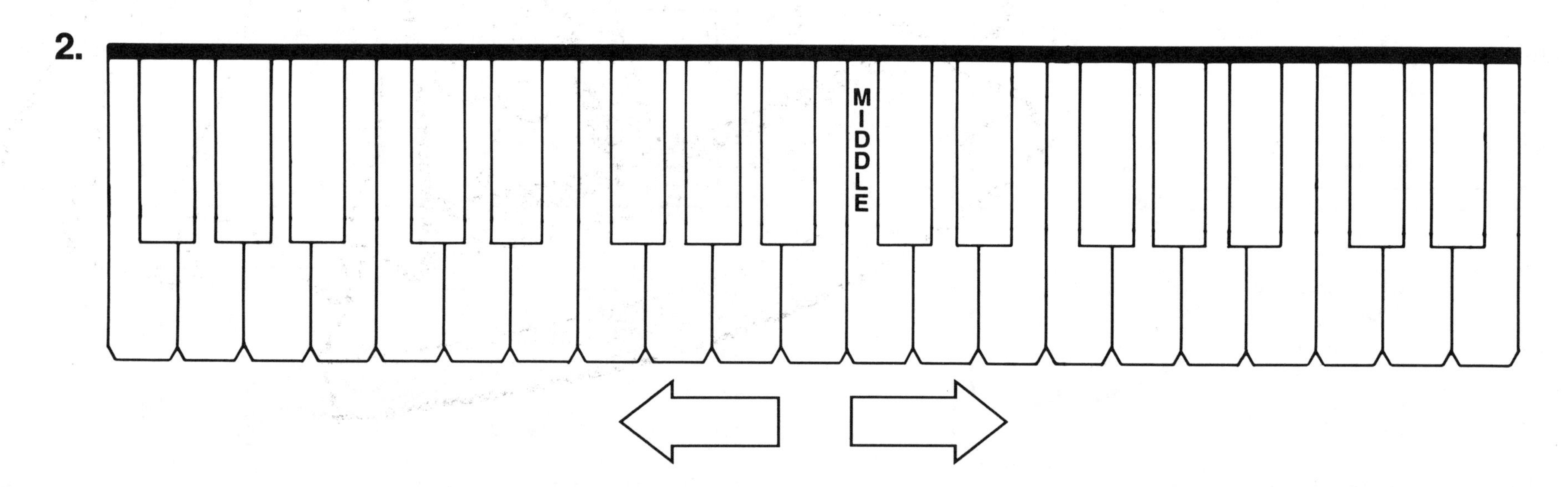

RAIN ON MY WINDOW PANE

GROUP 1 KEYS

Name the Group 1 keys and write letters on the keyboards to form their 5-finger positions.

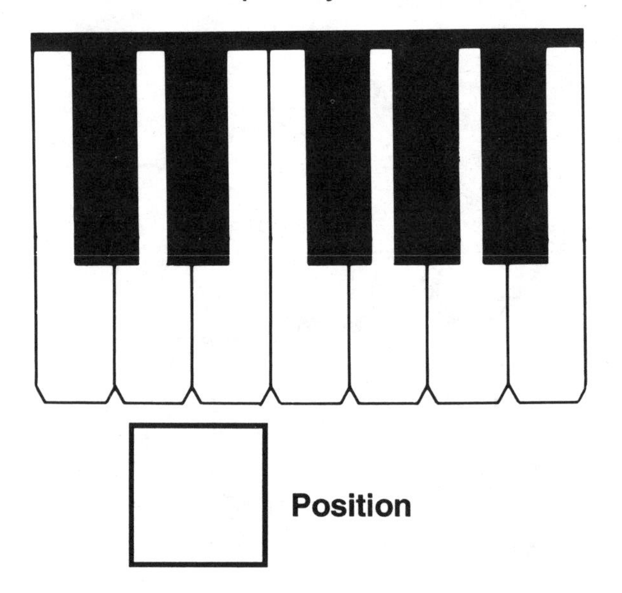

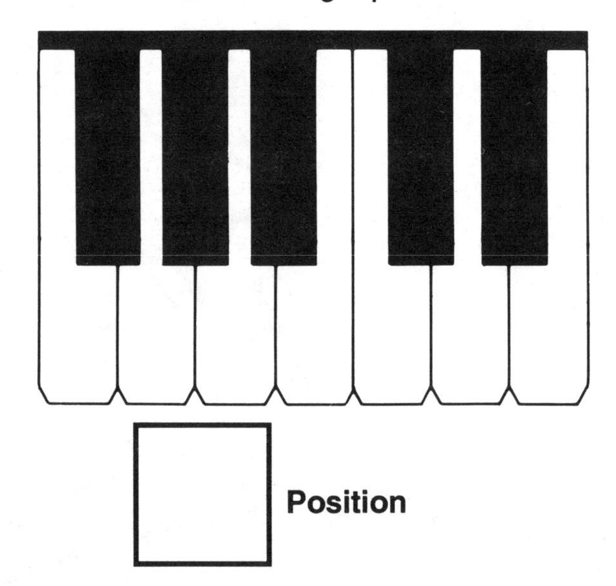

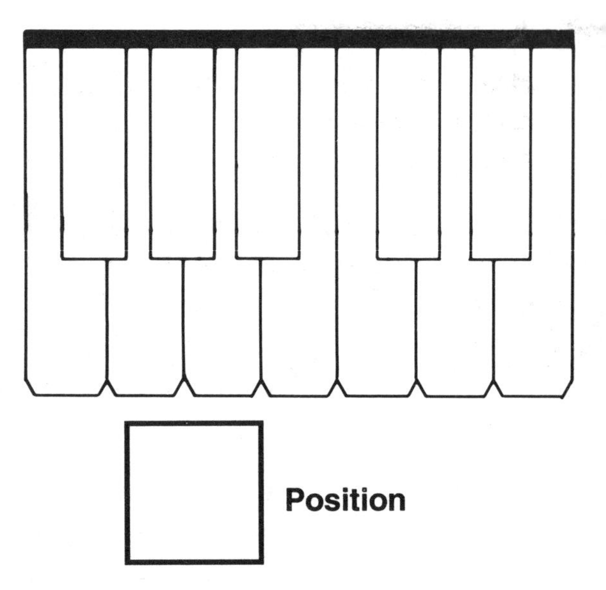

Position

Position

Position

1. Write letters inside the triangles to form each position.
2. Color the triangle black to show the black key in the F position.
3. Color the triangles red to form I chords for each position.
4. Circle the unusual position green.

C Position:

G Position:

F Position:

RECOGNIZING AND DRAWING CLEFS

UNIT 7
Teacher's Notes page 51

1. Color the hearts with:
   - treble clefs red
   - bass clefs pink

2. Circle the clefs where:
   - the right hand usually plays green
   - the left hand usually plays yellow

1. Trace the dotted lines to form the clefs.
2. Practice drawing clefs in the boxes.

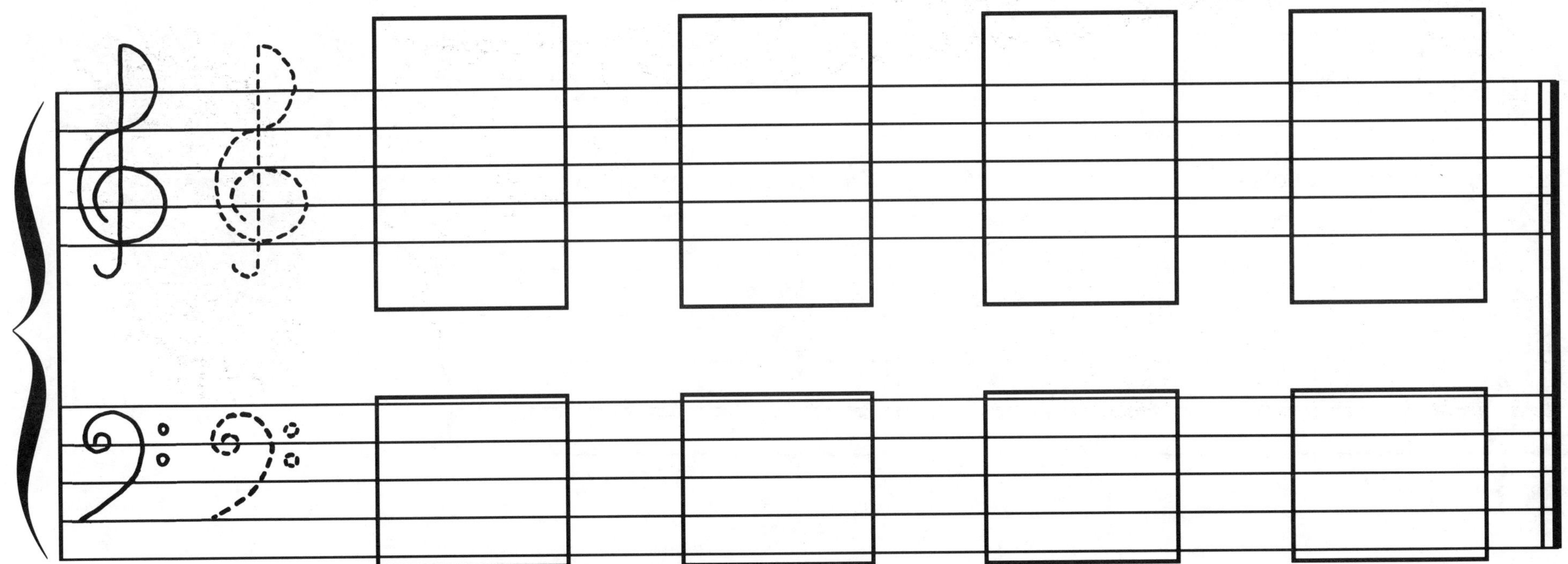

DRAWING LINE AND SPACE NOTES

Draw line notes (**L**) and space notes (**S**) on the grand staff.
Color: line notes orange   space notes green

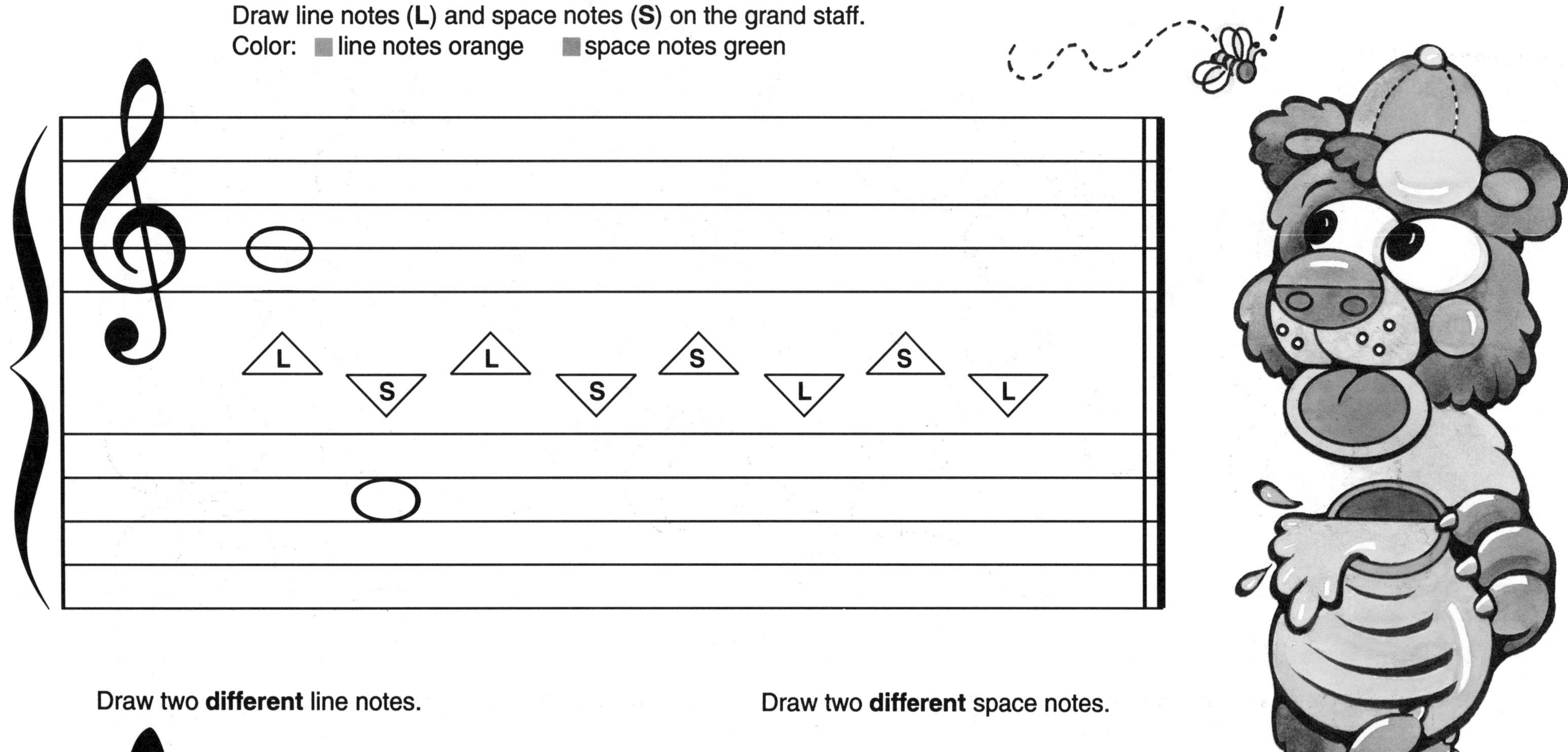

Draw two **different** line notes.

Draw two **different** space notes.

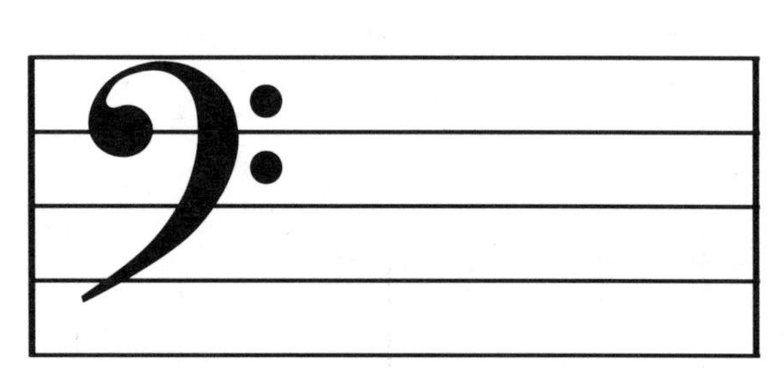

I AND V7 CHORDS IN F

A I chord has two skips.
A V7 chord has one step.

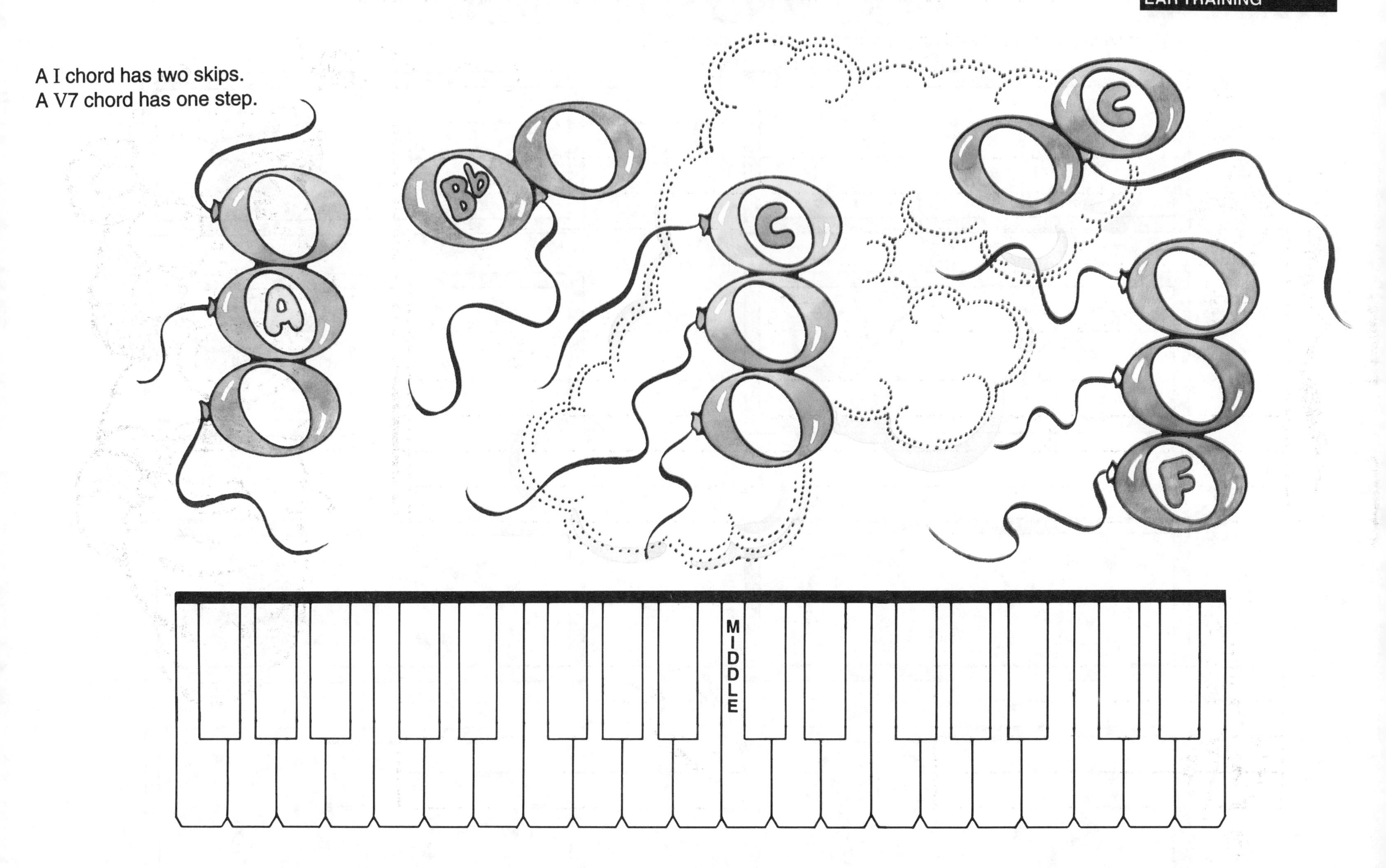

SAME AND DIFFERENT

1.

2.

3.

4.

I AND V7 CHORD SOUNDS

1.

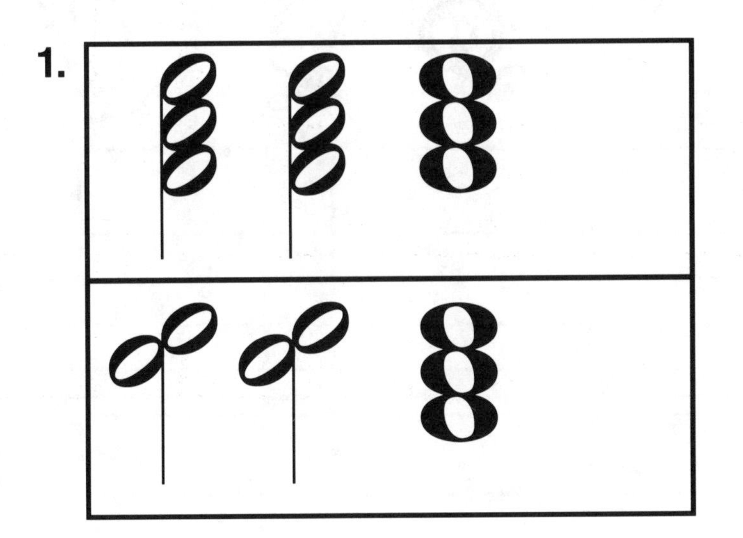

2.

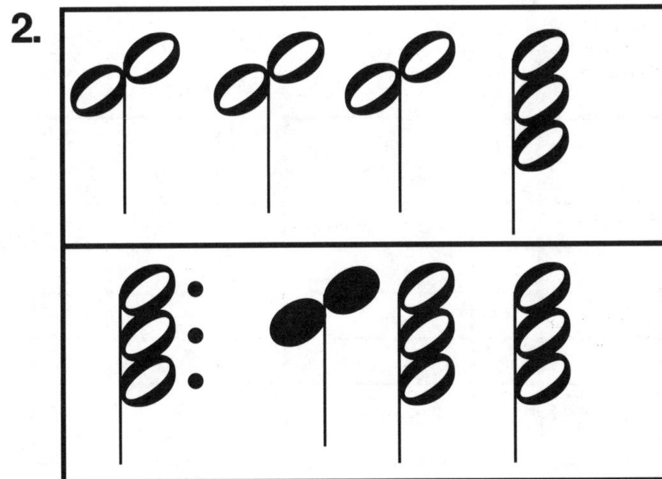

3.

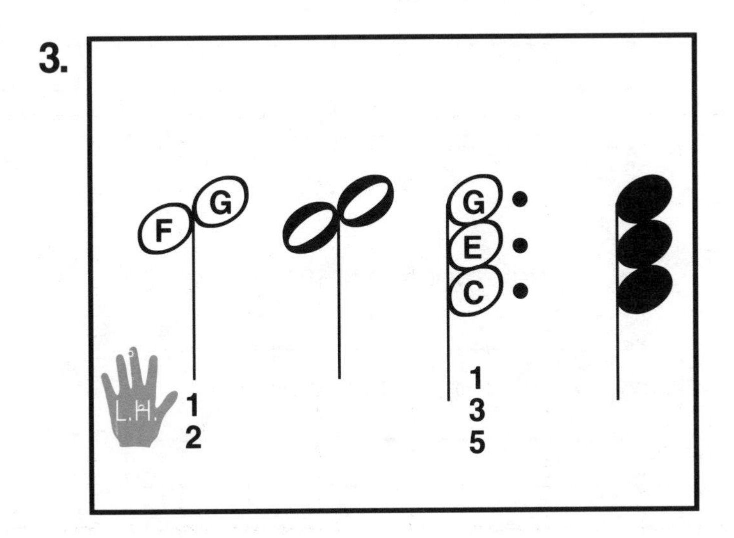

4.

DRAWING CLEFS

1. Trace the dotted lines to draw the grand staff and clefs.
2. Practice drawing clefs in the boxes.

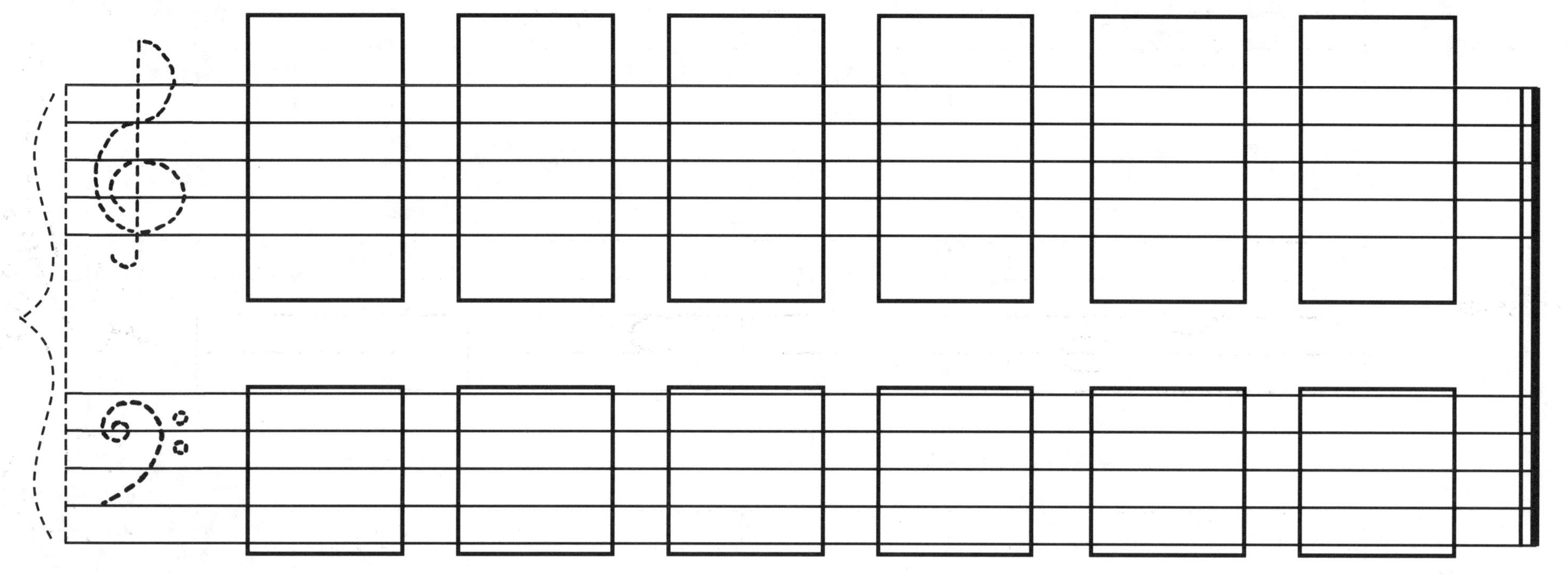

Draw two **different** space notes.

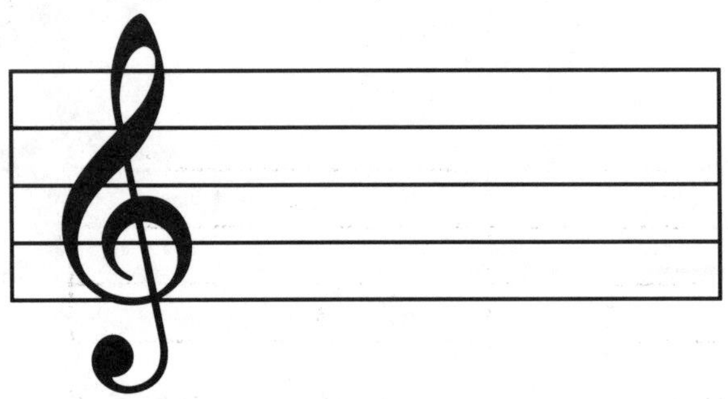

Draw two **different** line notes.

RECOGNIZING AND DRAWING SKIPS

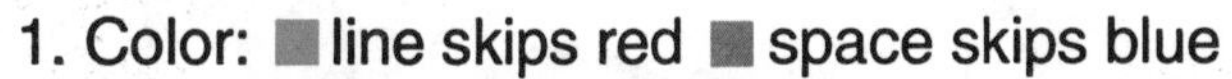

1. Color: line skips red · space skips blue
2. Circle the skips that: move up purple · move down green

Draw a treble clef

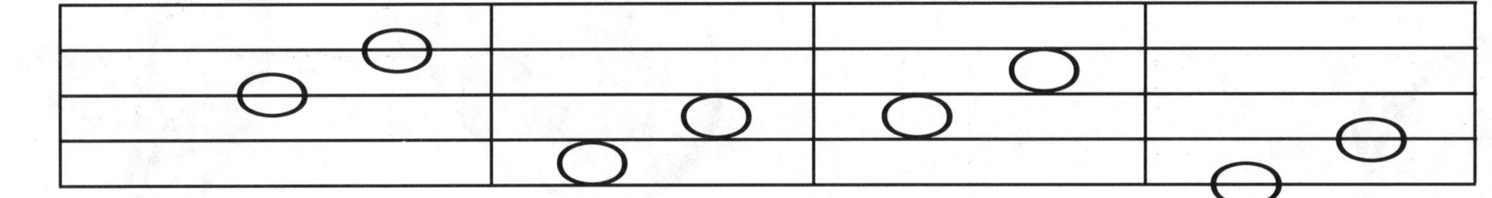

Draw a bass clef

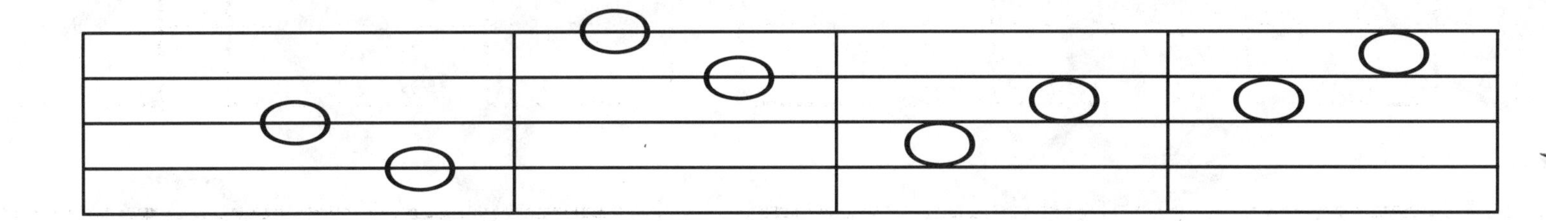

Draw skips **up** from the given notes.

Draw a treble clef

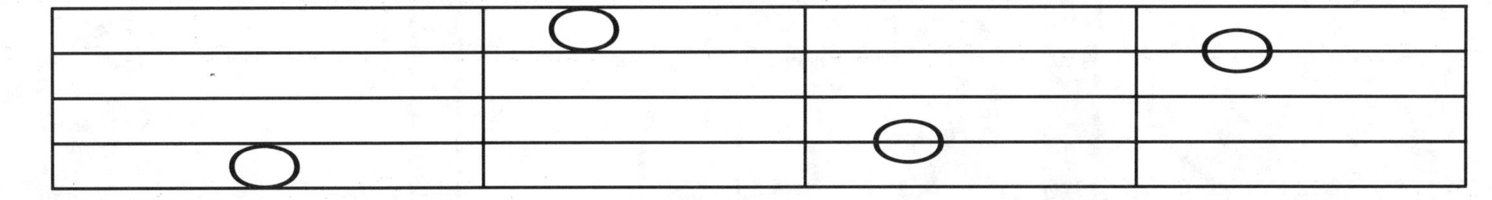

Draw skips **down** from the given notes.

Draw a bass clef

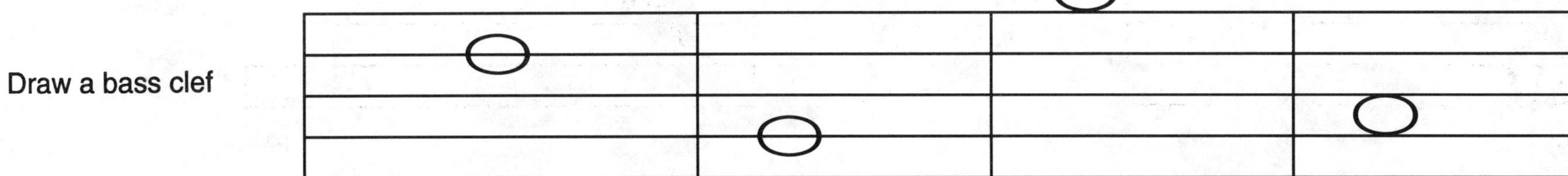

HATS OFF!

1. Think by steps and skips and fill in the missing letters in the chords.
2. Draw a line connecting each chord to its chord symbol.

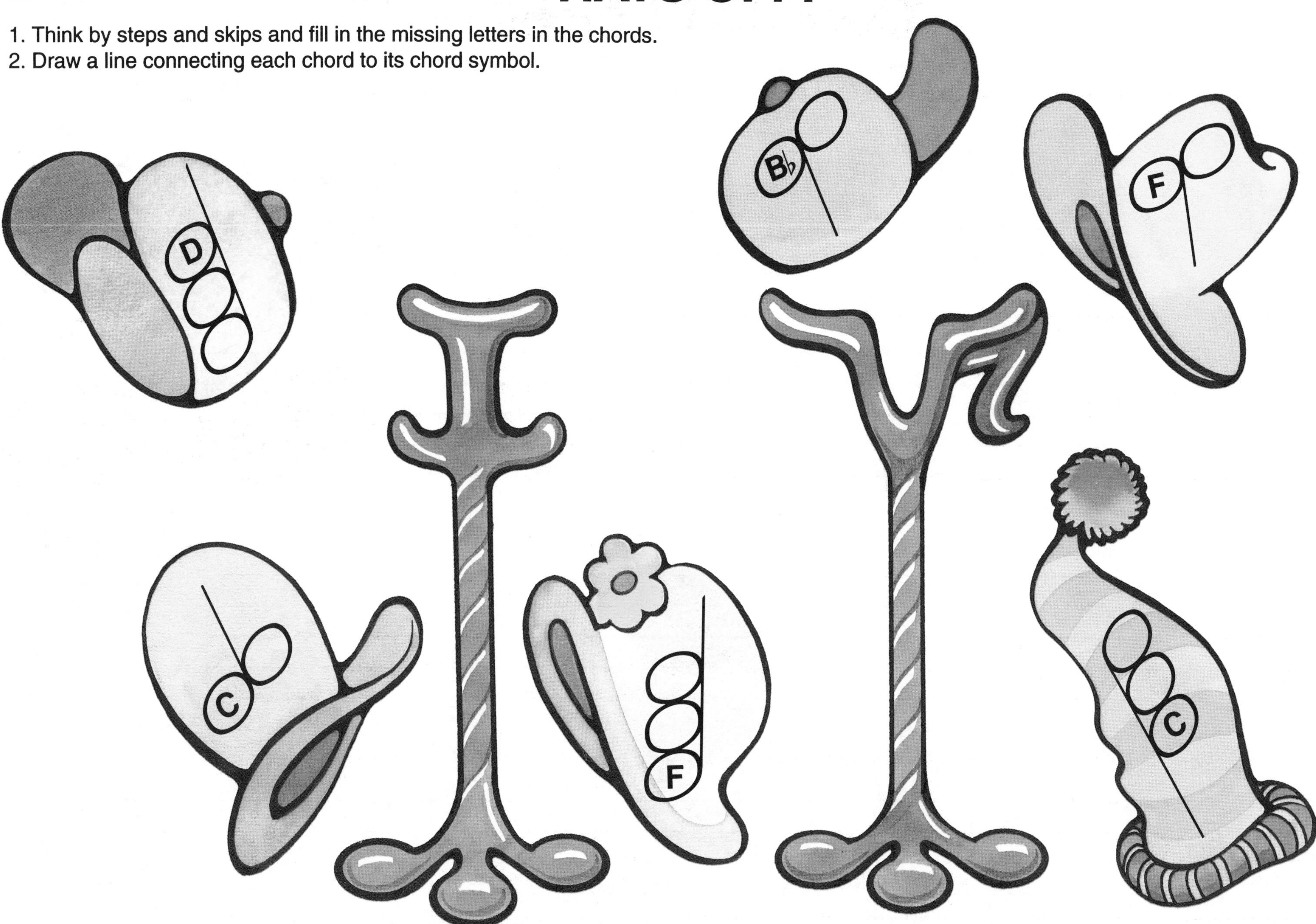

SUPER CHEF
POSITION: F
R.H.
Su - per chef! Su - per chef!
Sings his song in the key of F.

GRAND FINALE

1. Write letters to form steps or skips from the given letters as indicated.

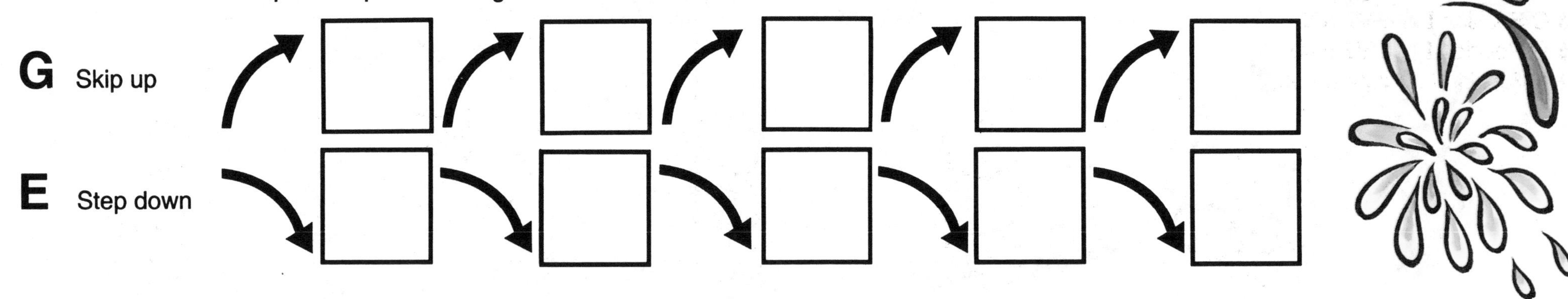

2. Write the letter names of the flats inside the triangles (include the flat sign).

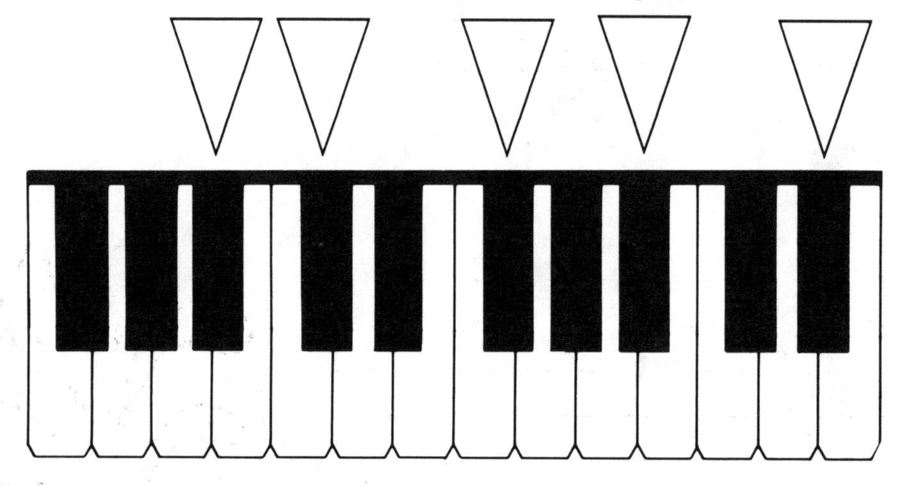

3. Draw the following notes:

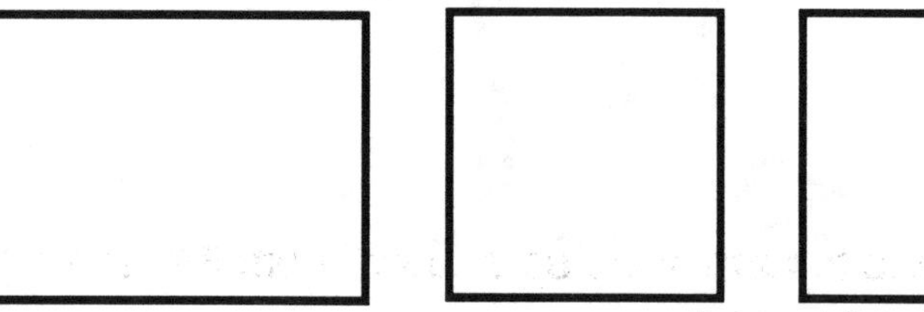

Three eighth notes | Eighth note | Dotted quarter note

4. Write letters to form the 5-finger positions. Color the keys to form I chords for each position. Circle the unusual position.

C

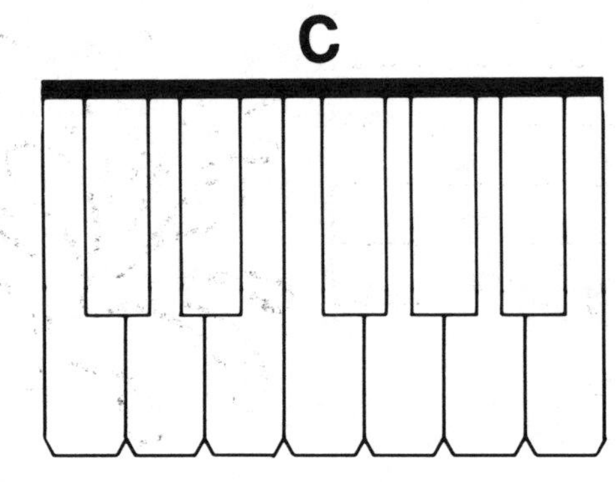

G

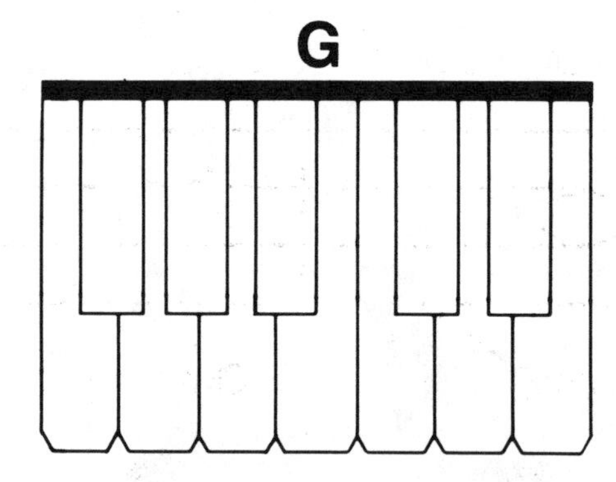

F

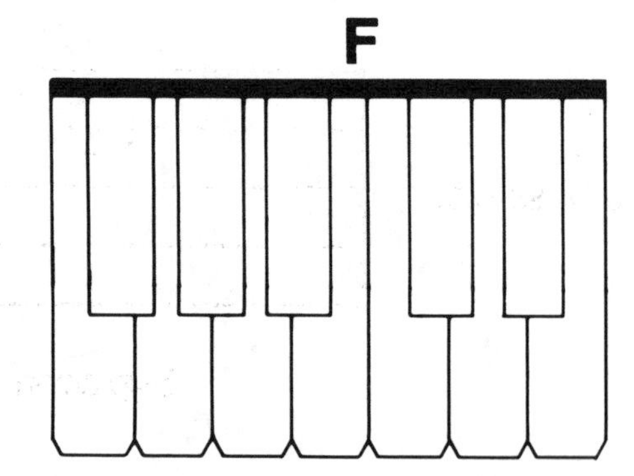

5. Think by steps or skips and fill in the missing letters in the chords.
Circle:
- C Position I and V7 red
- G Position I and V7 blue
- F Position I and V7 green

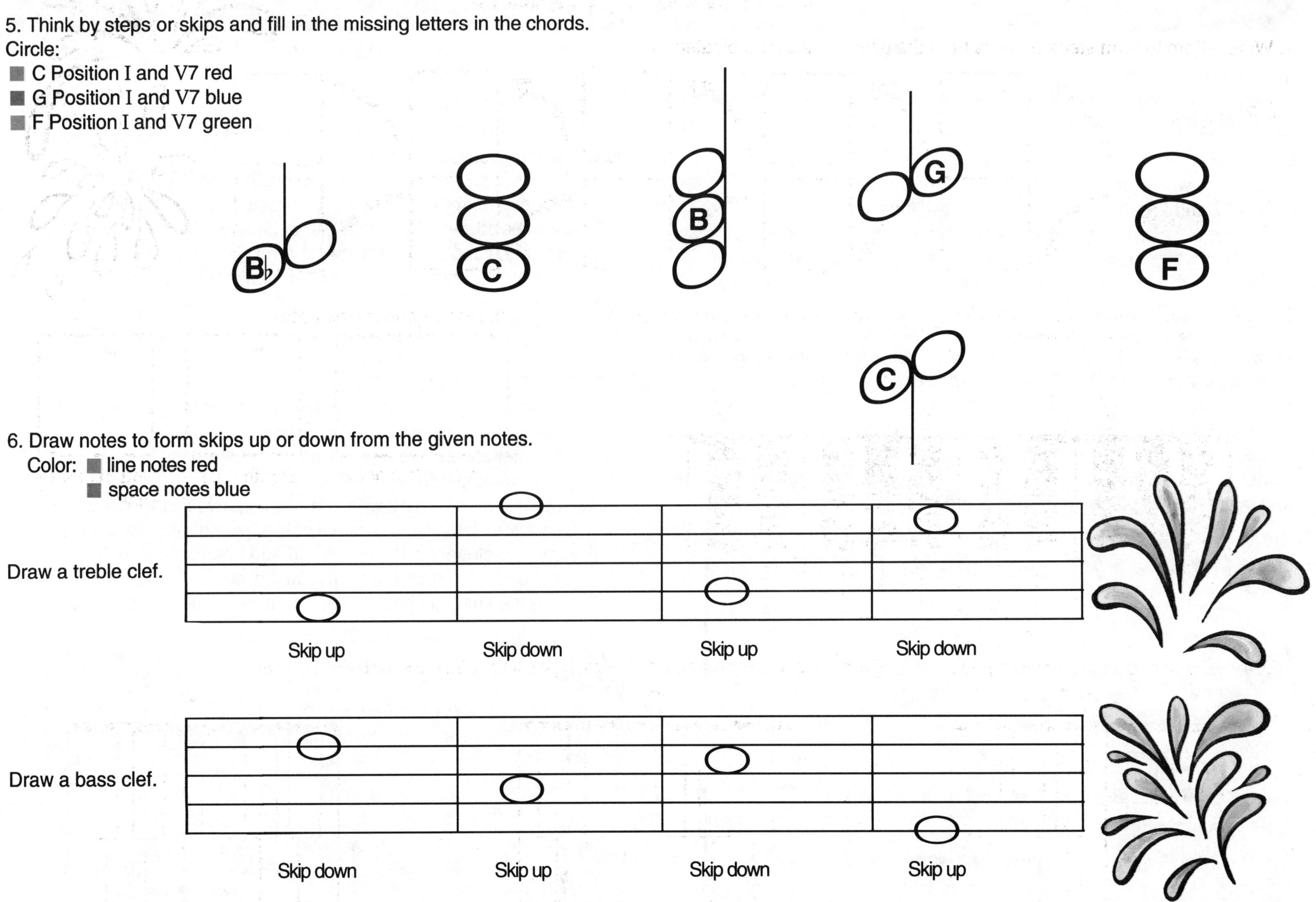

6. Draw notes to form skips up or down from the given notes.
Color:
- line notes red
- space notes blue

TEACHER'S NOTES

THEORY AND EAR TRAINING PARTY contains a variety of fun exercises to reinforce the concepts presented in *PIANO PARTY.* We suggest using these exercises with students after they have been introduced to the correlating weekly material in *PIANO PARTY.*

UNIT 1 (pages 2-7)

5 CHIMES

- Teach the words and music for the first three measures.
- Boxes 1 and 2: Play each example three times:
  1. Have the student sing with you as you play "Chimes" and listen to the rhythm of the "ding dongs" at the end of each example.
  2. Have the student listen again and circle the correct rhythm of "ding dongs."
  3. Have the student check his or her answer after the third hearing.
- Box 3: Have the student sing with you as you play "Chimes." Have the student play the "ding dong" part written in box 3 at the appropriate time and in the correct place on the keyboard.
- Box 4: Help the student create and notate a rhythm for the "ding dongs" in box 4. Have the student sing with you as you play "Chimes." Have the student play the "ding dong" part written in box 4 at the appropriate time and in the correct place on the keyboard.

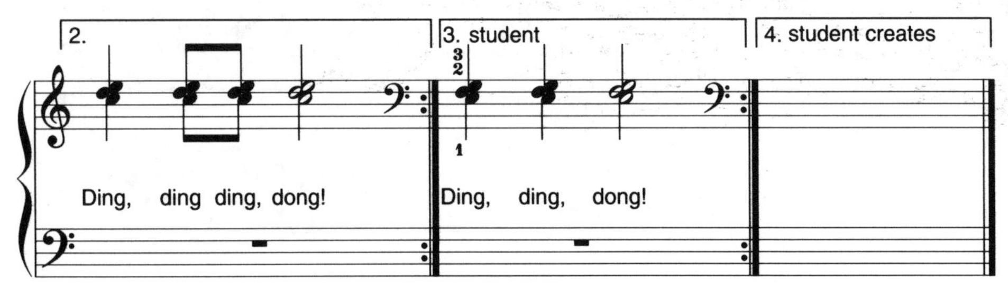

6 TEDDY BEAR'S RAINY DAY

- Have the student color the keys on all examples.
- Play each example three times:
  1. Have the student listen to determine the range (high or low) and color the appropriate picture (umbrella or teddy bear's boots).
  2. Have the student listen again to determine the direction (up or down) and circle the appropriate arrow below the keyboard.
  3. Have the student check his or her answer after the third playing.

7 THE WOODPECKER'S SONG

- Discuss the longer and shorter sounds of the notes in the pictures and have the student clap and count them aloud.
- Teach the melody and words for the first three measures.
- Play each example three times:
  1. Have the student sing with you as you play "The Woodpecker's Song" and listen to the rhythm of the "pecks" after each verse.
  2. Have the student listen again and add beams or fill in the noteheads to form the rhythm you played.
  3. Have the student check his or her answer after the third hearing.

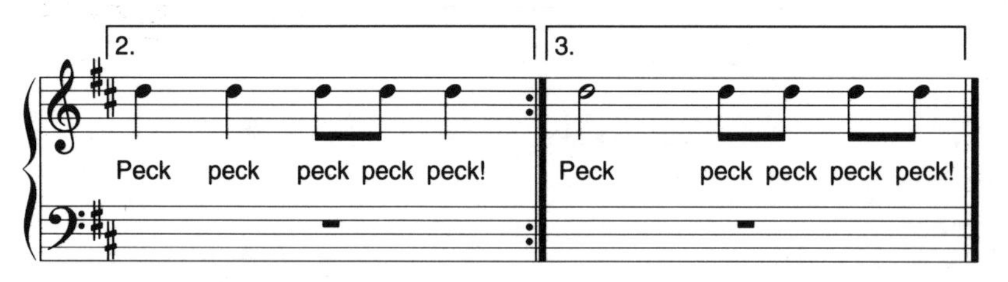

UNIT 2 (pages 8-12)

10 MATCHING C POSITIONS

- On both keyboards, have the student:
  1. Write the letters of the C 5-finger position three times.
  2. Circle the low C position red, the middle C position green, and the high C position blue.
- Play each example three times:
  1. Have the student listen and determine the range (low, middle, or high) and color the five appropriate keys.
  2. Have the student listen again and determine the direction (up or down) and circle the appropriate arrow.
  3. Have the student check his or her answer after the third hearing.

Note: There are two examples for each keyboard.

11 TAP AND CLAP FILL-INS

- A fun way to portray or feel rhythm is to have students tap and clap;
  X = clap hands together
  — = tap hands on the closed fallboard.
- Tap and clap each example three times:
  1. Have the student listen and repeat the taps and claps.
  2. Have the student listen again and fill in the missing notes.
  3. Have the student check his or her answer after the third hearing.

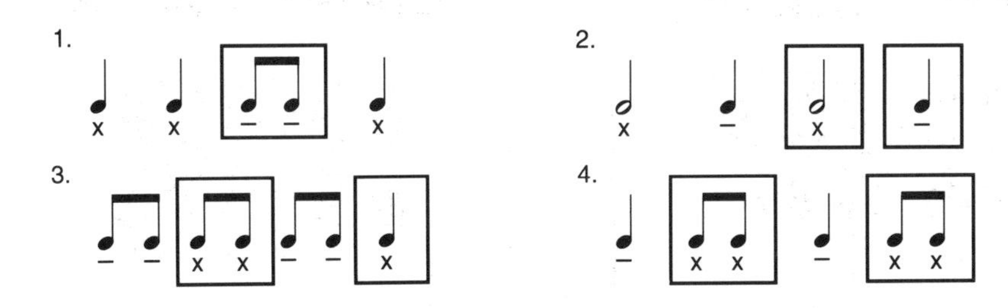

12 RECOGNIZING STEPS AND SKIPS

- Explain that there are two boxes for each example the student will hear
  1. One box of stairs has two adjacent figures on stairs which represent a step.
  2. The other box has two figures, separated by a stair, which represent a skip.
- Explain that you will play music to match **one** set of stairs (step or skip).
- Play each example three times:
  1. Have the student listen to determine whether you played a step or a skip.
  2. Have the student listen again and circle the appropriate set of stairs.
  3. Have the student check his or her answer after the third hearing.

Supplementary Activity

Ear Training Game: Matching Tones with Steps and Skips (works best with two keyboards)

- Identify the starting note and play a one or two measure melody in either the C or G 5-finger positions using steps or skips.
- Have the student repeat the melody you played on his or her keyboard.
- As new positions are introduced, repeat this activity in different keys.

UNIT 3 (pages 13-17)

15 WRITING AND HEARING C CHORDS

- Snowmen Fill-Ins: Explain that the I chord has two skips. Looking at the snowmen, help the student think by alphabet skips up or down from the given letter and fill in the missing letters to form C chords.
- Keyboard: Play each example three times:
  1. Have the student listen and determine the range (low, middle, or high).
  2. Have the student listen again and write the letter names of the C chord in the correct place on the keyboard.
  3. Have the student check his or her answer after the third hearing.

Supplementary Activity

Ear Training Game: Matching Chords (works best with two keyboards)

- Play I chords in a specific rhythm.
- Have the student listen and match your chords on his or her keyboard.
- When the V7 chord is introduced on page 37 in this book, you may want to extend this excercise by playing short progressions such as I V7 V7 I for the student to match.

16 MELODIC HOWLS

- Explain that the dogs on this page are musical. These dogs howl or sing melodies.
- Play each example four times:
  1. Have the student listen and determine the direction (up or down).
  2. Have the student listen again and determine the number of tones played.
  3. Have the student listen again and determine whether you played steps or skips and write the letter names on the keys.
  4. Have the student check his or her answer after the fourth hearing.

Note: Use the melodies provided or improvise your own to suit the needs and abilities of the student.

17 THE BLUEBIRD'S SONG

- Teach the words and music for the first three measures.
- Boxes 1 and 2: Play each example three times:
  1. Have the student sing with you as you play "The Bluebird's Song" and listen to the rhythm of the "tweets" at the end of each example.
  2. Have the student listen again and circle the correct rhythm of "tweets."
  3. Have the student check his or her answer after the third hearing.
- Box 3: Have the student sing with you as you play "The Bluebird's Song." Have the student play the "tweet" part written in box 3 at the appropriate time and in the correct place on the keyboard.
- Box 4: Help the student create and notate a rhythm for the "tweets" in box 4. Have the student sing with you as you play "The Bluebird's Song." Have the student play the "tweet" part in box 4 at the appropriate time and in the correct place on the keyboard.

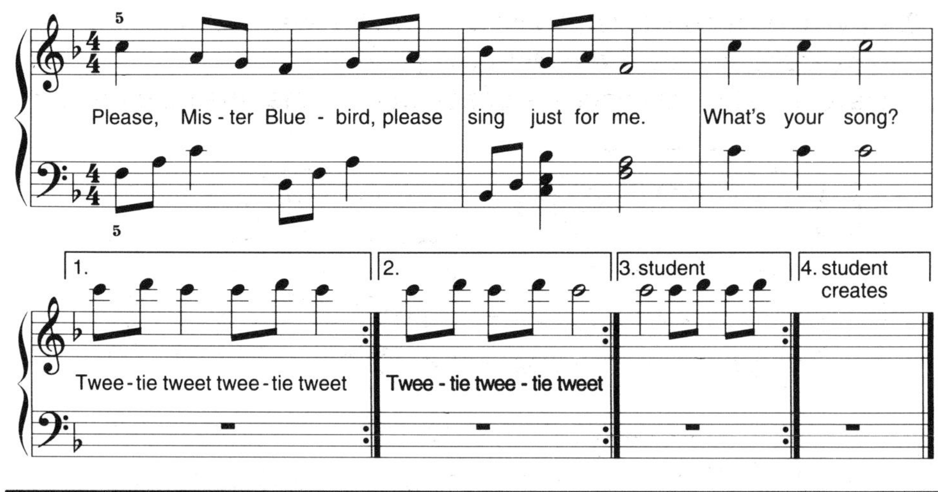

UNIT 4 (pages 18-22)

20 MATCHING G POSITIONS

- On both keyboards, have the student:
  1. Write the letters of the G 5-finger position three times.
  2. Circle the low G position red, the middle G position green, and the high G position blue.
- Play each example three times:
  1. Have the student listen and determine the range (low, middle, or high) and color the five appropriate keys.
  2. Have the student listen again and determine the direction (up or down) and circle the appropriate arrow.
  3. Have the student check his or her answer after the third hearing.

Note: There are two examples for each keyboard.

21 BOOGIE WOOGIE BUNNY

- Discuss the longer and shorter sounds of the notes in the picture and have the student clap and count them aloud.
- Teach the melody and words for the first three measures.
- Play each example three times:
  1. Have the student sing with you as you play "Boogie Woogie Bunny" and listen to the rhythm of the "hops" after each verse.

2. Have the student listen again and add beams or fill in the noteheads to form the rhythm you played.
3. Have the student check his or her answer after the third hearing.

22 HANDY ANDY

- Teach the words and music for the first three measures.
- Boxes 1 and 2: Play each example three times:
    1. Have the student sing with you as you play "Handy Andy" and listen to the rhythm of the "bangs" at the end of each example.
    2. Have the student listen again and circle the correct rhythm of "bangs."
    3. Have the student check his or her answer after the third hearing.
- Box 3: Have the student sing with you as you play "Handy Andy." Have the student play the "bang" part written in box 3 at the appropriate time and in the correct place on the keyboard.
- Box 4: Help the student create and notate a rhythm for the "bangs" in box 4. Have the student sing with you as you play "Handy Andy." Have the student play the "bang" part in box 4 at the appropriate time and in the correct place on the keyboard.

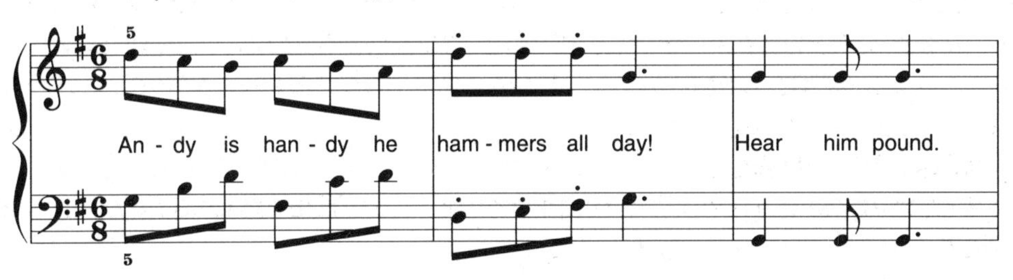

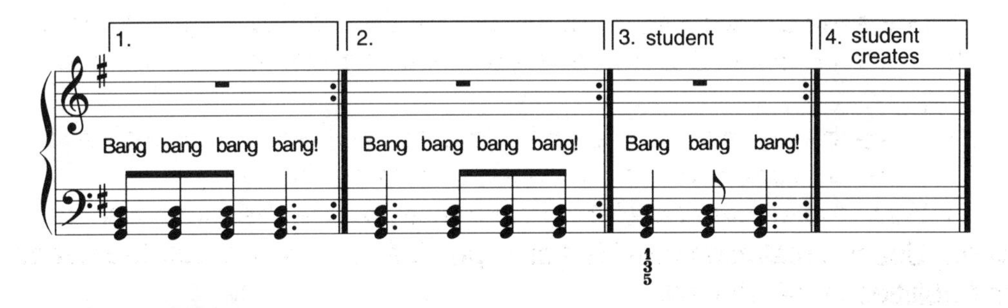

UNIT 5 (pages 23-27)

25 WRITING AND HEARING G CHORDS

- Life Preserver Fill-Ins: Explain that the I chord has two skips. Looking at the life preservers, help the student think by alphabet skips up or down from the given letter and fill in the missing letters to form G chords.
- Keyboard: Play each example three times:
    1. Have the student listen and determine the range (low, middle, or high.)
    2. Have the student listen again and write the letter names of the G chord in the correct place on the keyboard.
    3. Have the student check his or her answer after the third hearing.

26 MELODIC MEOWS

• Explain that the cats on this page are musical. These cats meow or sing melodies.

• Play each example four times:

1. Have the student listen and determine the direction (up or down).
2. Have the student listen again and determine the number of tones played.
3. Have the student listen again and determine whether you played steps or skips and write the letter names on the keys.
4. Have the student check his or her answer after the fourth hearing.

Note: Use the melodies provided or improvise your own to suit the needs and abilities of the student.

27 GIFTS OF MUSIC

• Explain that the storks are holding bags filled with gifts of music. Some of the gifts are filled with notes but some are empty. The empty packages are to be filled in with notes by the student based on the following listening examples.

• Discuss the longer and shorter sounds of the notes in the pictures and have the student clap and count them aloud.

• Teach the melody and words for the first measure.

• Play each example three times:

1. Have the student sing with you as you play "Gifts of Music" and listen to the rhythm of the "la's" after each verse.
2. Have the student listen again and write in the notes to form the correct rhythm.
3. Have the student check his or her answer after the third hearing.

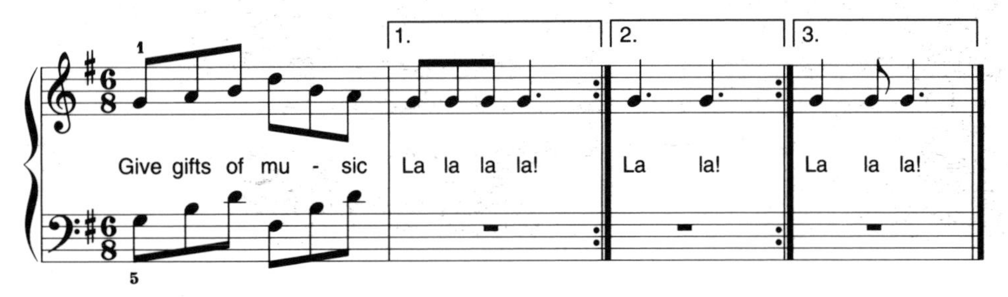

UNIT 6 (pages 28-33)

31 SAME AND DIFFERENT

• Explain that there are two boxes for each music example the student will hear:

One box has two figures that are the same.

The other box has two figures that are different.

• Explain that you will play two phrases for each example. If the second phrase is the same as the first, have the student color the figures in the "same" box. If the second phrase is different, have the student color the figures in the "different" box.

• If the examples are different, help the student to identify what was different— melody, rhythm, articulation.

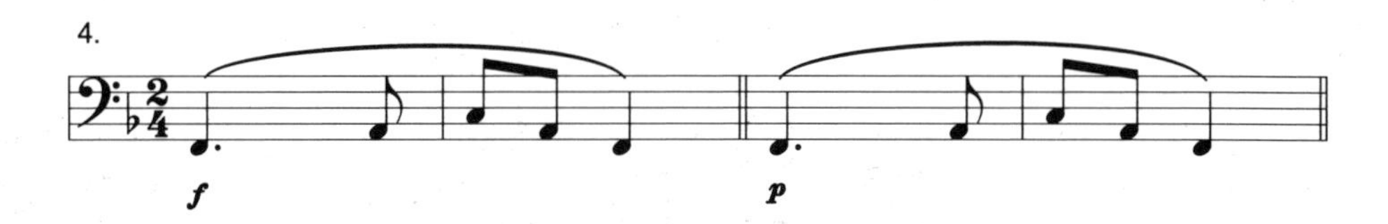

32 MATCHING F POSITIONS

- On both keyboards, have the student:
  1. Write the letters of the F 5-finger position three times.
  2. Circle the low F position red, the middle F position green, and the high F position blue.
- Play each example three times:
  1. Have the student listen and determine the range (low, middle, or high) and color the five appropriate keys.
  2. Have the student listen again and determine the direction (up or down) and circle the appropriate arrow.
  3. Have the student check his or her answer after the third hearing.

Note: There are two examples for each keyboard.

33 RAIN ON MY WINDOW PANE

- Discuss the longer and shorter sounds of the notes in the picture and have the student clap and count them aloud.
- Teach the melody and words for the first measure.
- Play each example three times:
  1. Have the student sing with you as you play "Rain On My Window Pane" and listen to the rhythm of the "drip drops" after each verse.
  2. Have the student listen again and add beams or fill in the noteheads to form the rhythm you played.
  3. Have the student check his or her answer after the third hearing.

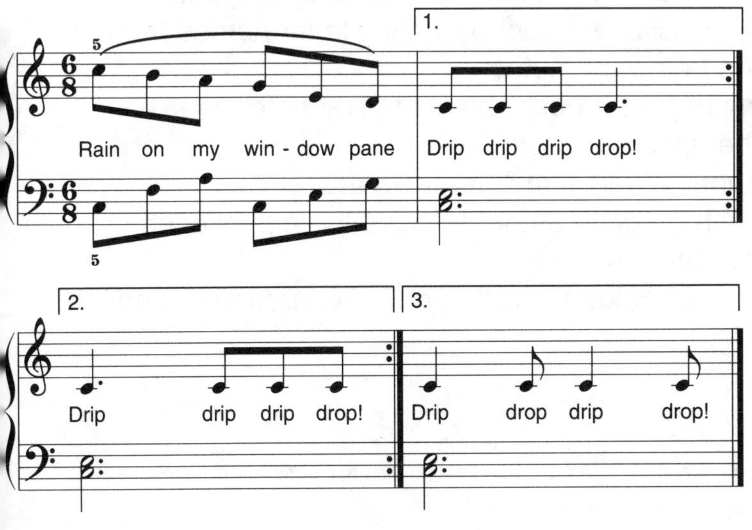

UNIT 7 (pages 34-39)

35 RECOGNIZING AND DRAWING CLEFS

- Steps to draw the treble clef are shown on this page.
- We relate these steps to drawing letters in the alphabet:
  1. Draw a large "J"—start above the staff and end below it.
  2. From the top of the J, draw a "D" to the fourth line (counting up from the bottom line).
  3. From the fourth line, draw a "C" to the first line.
  4. Continue up from the first line and draw a curl that wraps around the second line on the staff.

37 I AND V7 CHORDS IN F

- Chord Fill-Ins: Explain that the V7 chord has one step. Discuss the difference between the I and V7 chord shapes. Looking at the chords, help the student think by alphabet steps or skips up or down from the given letters and fill in the missing letter(s).
- Keyboard: Play each example three times:
  1. Have the student listen to determine the range (low, middle, or high).
  2. Have the student listen again and write the letter names of the F chord (I or V7) in the correct place on the keyboard.
  3. Have the student check his or her answer after the third hearing.

38 SAME AND DIFFERENT

• Explain that there are two boxes for each music example the student will hear:

One box has two figures that are the same.

The other box has two figures that are different.

• Explain that you will play two phrases for each example. If the second phrase is the same as the first, have the student color the figures in the "same" box. If the second phrase is different, have the student color the figures in the "different" box.

• If the examples are different, help the student to identify what was different— melody, rhythm, articulation.

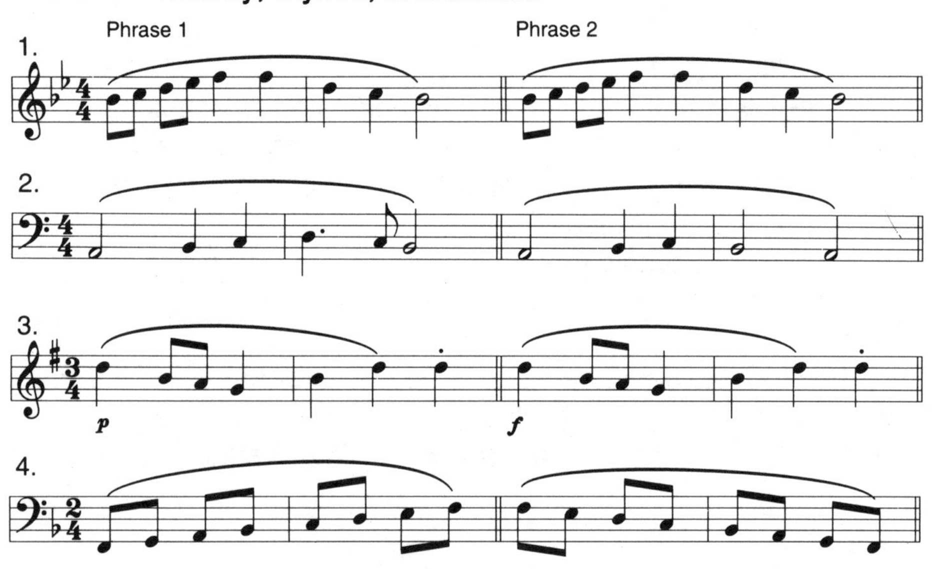

39 I AND V7 CHORD SOUNDS

• Discuss the difference in sound between I and V7 chords.

• Play either I or V7 chords and have the student identify them by listening.

• Teach the words and music for the first two measures.

• Boxes1 and 2: Play each example three times:

1. Have the student sing with you as you play "I and V7 Chord Sounds" and listen to the chord progression at the end of each example.
2. Have the student listen again and circle the correct chords.
3. Have the student check his or her answer after the third hearing.

• Box 3: Have the student sing with you as you play "I and V7 Chord Sounds." Have the student play the chords written in box 3 at the appropriate time and in the correct place on the keyboard.

• Box 4: Help the student create and notate a rhythm for the chords in box 4. Have the student sing with you as you play "I and V7 Chord Sounds." Have the student play the chords in box 4 at the appropriate time and in the correct place on the keyboard.

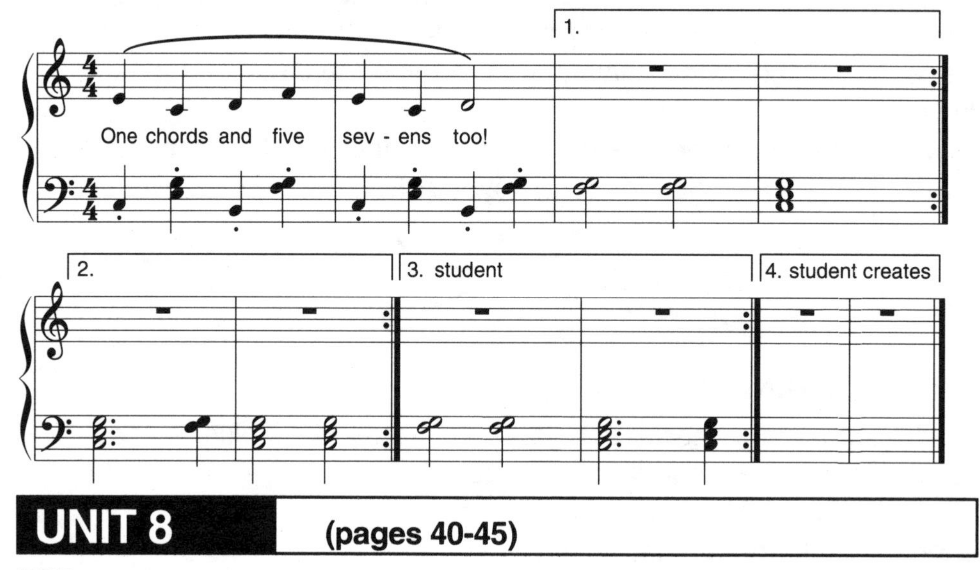

UNIT 8 (pages 40-45)

43 SUPER CHEF

• Teach the words to the song.

• Help the student:

1. Determine the rhythm that fits the words.
2. Fill in the noteheads and add beams to notate the rhythm.
3. Create a melody for "Super Chef" by writing letter names from the F 5-finger position below the notes.
4. Write the starting finger number above the first note.
5. Practice his or her piece.
6. Improvise different melodies for "Super Chef."

• If you are working with a group of students, have them play each other's pieces as well as their own.

• You may wish to help your students add I and V7 chords to harmonize their melodies. Example:

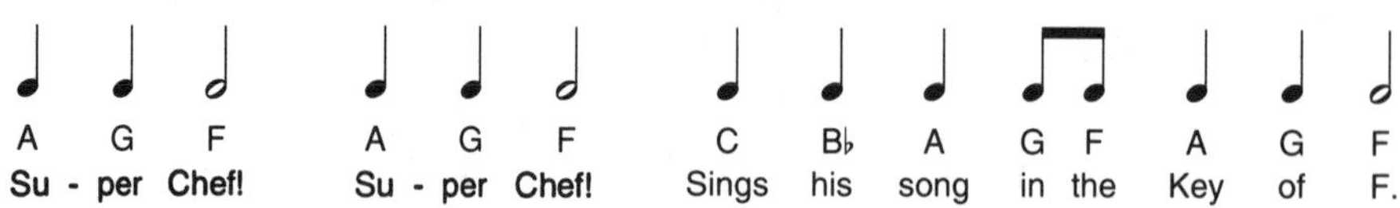